Beachcomber's Guide to Gulf Coast Marine Life

Lone Star Books
A Division of Gulf Publishing Company
Houston, London, Paris, Tokyo

Beachcomber's Guide to Gulf Coast Marine Life

Nick Fotheringham

**with contributions by
Susan Brunenmeister
and Patsy Menefee**

Beachcomber's Guide to Gulf Coast Marine Life

Library of Congress Cataloging in Publication Data

Fotheringham, Nick.
    Beachcomber's guide to Gulf Coast marine life.

    Bibliography: p.
    Includes index.
    1. Marine invertebrates—Mexico, Gulf of.
2. Seashore biology—Mexico, Gulf of.
I. Brunenmeister, Susan Lee. II. Menefee, Patsy.
III. Title.
QL134.F66   592.0976   80-10607
ISBN 0-88415-062-3

Book Design by
Leigh Owen

Contents

Preface

This guide was designed as an aid to the student, fisherman or beachcomber who wishes to become acquainted with the spectacular array of invertebrate animals living along the Gulf shore. The organisms described in this introductory guide are those which we believe are commonly encountered by the casual observer. The list of Gulf Coast invertebrates is by no means complete, and therefore, this guide should not be used as a taxonomic reference by the serious student of marine invertebrates. However, systematic sources for many taxa are included in the bibliography.

We wish to acknowledge the help of the numerous students of invertebrate zoology and marine biology at the University of Houston who assisted in making the collections on which this guide is based. We are especially indebted to B.R. Collins, proprietor of the West Bay Bait Camp, and to Archie Curl, a Texas City shrimp fisherman, for the generous use of their facilities for the collection of specimens. We thank Carl L. Thurman, J.B. Wills and Ruth Ann Bagnall for their help in identifying fiddler crabs, polychaetes and zooplankters, respectively. We are also indebted to many friends, especially Drs. Sewell H. Hopkins, Harold W. Harry and Frank Fisher, for their numerous suggestions during the preparation of the manuscript. Conversations with Charles Allen, James Baker, Marion Johnson, Maurice Jones, Mary Kutac, Gary Penn, and Tom Scanland contributed greatly to the revision of this guide. We greatly appreciate the use of facilities of the University of Houston Coastal Center during our study of this fauna. We are also indebted to Anne Fotheringham for her typing skills and many helpful hints.

We would also like to thank Miss Patsy Menefee for her excellent drawings. All of the illustrations were drawn by Miss Menefee except the following, which were drawn by the authors: 1.1, 1.2, 2.1, 2.2, 2.13, 2.20-2.26, 3.1, 3.4, 3.6, 3.10, 3.13, 3.14, 3.16, 3.17, 3.32, 3.37-3.40, 4.1-4.6, 4.9, 4.13, 4.14, 5.1-5.29, 5.34-5.50, 6.4, 6.10, 6.13, 7.3, 7.13. 7.20-7.26, 7.31, 7.34, 8.1-8.29, 8.31-8.48, 9.3, 9.6, 9.7, 10.2, 10.3, 10.5, 10.7, 11.1-11.13 (N. Fotheringham) and 2.4, 2.10, 2.16, 2.19, 3.20-3.23, 3.36, 3.42, 3.43, 4.12, 4.15, 5.30-5.32, 5.51, 6.6, 6.8, 6.11, 6.12, 7.5, 7.6, 7.8, 7.10-7.12, 7.19, 7.35, 9.2, 9.4, 9.5, 10.1 (S. Brunenmeister).

Introduction

Exploring the beach brings endless fascination and intrigue. Each breaking wave sweeps away the old beach face and unveils an array of curiosities. Forces staggering in variety and intensity abuse animal life along the beach, yet life clings to the shore and adapts. Crushing waves and the scouring currents they generate, the continuously changing tides, the baking sun, shorebirds probing with long bills and little fish darting into the shallows between waves all take their toll. The survivors have evolved with a special blend of characteristics that make survival in such an inhospitable environment possible. What reward could have stimulated such an effort?

The sea is the birthplace of life; the ancestors of many millions of inhabitants of forests and lakes emerged from the sea eons ago. The land promised new frontiers and a haven from old enemies for creatures from the sea. But the sea is a temptress, luring back the children of its emigrants with morsels of food cast upon the shore and the promise of more just beneath her surface. However, the seashore is a boundary that is often assailed but seldom bridged. Many have risen to her bait, but few have found its source and lived. Thus the beach is a zone of conflict, an arena for developing peculiar life-styles by species from both the sea and the land.

The most striking results of these experiments in living are found among the invertebrates. They exhibit many of nature's most exotic life-styles. The invertebrates of the sea include species that can jump fifty times their own length, carry many times their own weight, bore into solid rock, change sex at will, change color to match their background, lay as many as half a billion eggs at one time or regrow a head that has been cut off. These unusual abilities are adaptations to an unusual environment.

No special knowledge is required to discover the numerous intriguing secrets of these animals. Many engrossing hours may be spent at the seashore discovering how a mole crab burrows, how a ghost crab signals with its claws, how a sea anemone moves a bit of food placed on a tentacle to its mouth, how a barnacle captures food with its feet, how male fiddler crabs fight for possession of a burrow or how an oyster drill drills an oyster. This book is a guide to the life-styles of more than 300 of the most common invertebrates that the visitor to the shores of the northwestern Gulf of Mexico is likely to encounter. It includes points of interest and ways to observe that will make a visit to the beach an enriching experience.

Unfortunately, many of the creatures cast at the feet of beachcombers have been torn from their usual habitats and lifestyles and are often lifeless, broken, or faded. Through the chapters on offshore habitats the reader is transported to the environments in which these animals display morphological and behavioral adaptations seldom evident in beachwashed specimens.

Readers who are not familiar with our system of biological classification may wish to read the brief guide in Appendix I on page 101.

1

General Shore and Faunal Features

The Habitats

The predominant coastal form along the northwestern coast of the Gulf of Mexico consists of a series of barrier islands enclosing several shallow bays (Figure 1.1). These islands and bays encompass a mosaic of marine and estuarine habitats which differ in substrate, exposure to surf, food resources and environmental variability. Habitats on the outer side of the barrier islands receive more abuse from waves but undergo less abrupt changes in salinity and temperature than do habitats on the bay side of the islands. Sandy beaches and rock jetties are the major habitat types on the outer coast; mud flats, salt marshes, pilings and oyster reefs are the major habitat types in the bays (Figure 1.2). The water itself forms an additional habitat for swimming and floating organisms.

The jetties at Port Arthur, Galveston, Freeport, Port Aransas and Port Isabel and the numerous groins along the Galveston seawall were designed to modify the pattern of nearshore circulation along the coast. They interrupt the flow of sand along the shore, thus reducing the erosion of adjacent beaches and the deposition of sand in navigation channels. Consequently, these structures and the organisms living on them are subjected to breaking waves laden with sand, strong currents, and fluctuating sand levels. On the other hand, these waves bring moisture to organisms living high on the jetties, and the currents bring plankton, the microscopic life consumed by most of the jetty inhabitants.

Organisms living on the sandy beaches along the Gulf side of the barrier islands must also contend with surf, currents, and shifting sand. Most sandy-beach animals escape the physical hazards of their environ-

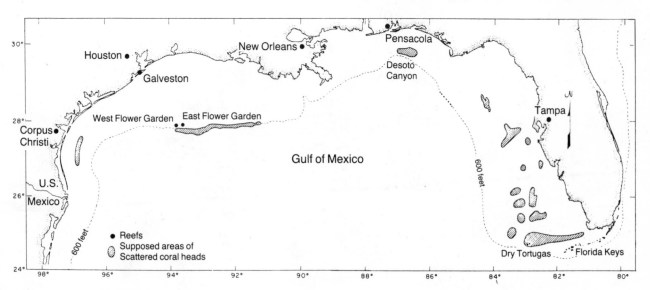

Figure 1.1. Northern Gulf Coast.

ment by burrowing. Thus, almost the entire community lives underground—and out of sight. Some species minimize the changes in their environment by migrating up and down the beach with the changing tide. Others avoid the surf by living high on the beach and returning to the sea only to wet their gills or to forage for bits of food left by the ebbing tide. Still others have very large gills to supply oxygen for the extra exertion demanded by a life in the surf zone or tufts of hairlike setae to protect sensitive structures from the constantly moving sand.

The barrier islands protect habitats in the bays from the severest effects of waves and currents. As a result of the slowed water movement, fine particles passing down the rivers and bayous into the bays settle to the bottom, producing a muddier substrate than is found on the outer shore. Moreover, the bays are shallow. They heat and cool faster and undergo more abrupt changes in salinity and oxygen content.

The relatively stable and extensive soft bottom of the bays provides an ideal environment for numerous burrowing animals. Their major obstacle is the hydrogen sulfide layer, a toxic layer of generally black mud characterized by an odor like that of rotting eggs, which forms at shallower depths in the bays than in the more turbulent outer coast habitats. Due to the shallowness of the bays, broad mud flats are exposed during low tides, leaving nonburrowing species at the mercy of predators and the drying sun. Salt tolerant plants known as halophytes may become established on the edges of these flats. These plants further impede the circulation near them, which causes additional sediment to be deposited during high tides. In

this manner salt marshes develop around the bay, and small islands may become established within the bay.

Two other submerged habitat types are commonly found within the bays: grass flats and oyster reefs. The grass flats on the northwestern Gulf Coast consist primarily of shoal grass, *Halodule wrightii,* or turtle grass, *Thalassia testudinum,* which, like the salt marsh, helps to stabilize the soft bottom. These grasses build low mounds by trapping sediment among their roots. Because they require light for photosynthesis, grass flats are only found in shallow water.

Oyster reefs, on the other hand, are composed of animals which do not depend directly on sunlight. Oysters are therefore nearly independent of water depth, but depend heavily on food-carrying currents. They secrete calcareous shells which they cement to those of adjacent oysters, producing a massive habitat suitable to numerous other species.

The northern Gulf Coast has a highly variable climate. Hurricanes, northers, freshets and freezes are sporadic events that may have tremendous effects on shore species. Animals dwelling near the waterline risk exposure to large and often abrupt changes in temperature, salinity and water level caused by these events. Hurricanes and severe thunderstorms dump enormous quantities of water on the coastal zone, most of which runs off into the bays and then through the passes into the Gulf. Because it is lighter than sea water, much of this fresh water flows along the surface without mixing very deeply into the bays. However, the salinity along the shoreline will be reduced for several days and the water level will be higher than normal. Hurricanes may also alter coastal morphol-

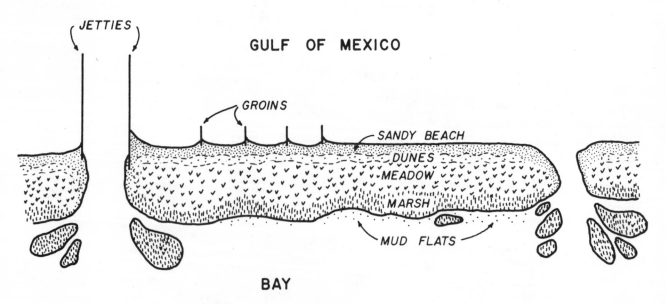

Figure 1. 2. Locations of major coastal habitats on a barrier island.

ogy and consequently the patterns of nearshore water circulation.

Northers blow the surface water away from the coast and sharply reduce the air temperature, chilling animals exposed by the receding water level. Some species escape these stresses by burrowing into the sediment or by migrating into deeper water; others are physiologically versatile and are able to adjust to short-term alterations of their environment. Compound events, such as a freeze and a norther occurring simultaneously, stress nearshore animals more than either single event.

On the average, however, the northern coast of the Gulf of Mexico is a warm, humid subtropical region. Mean air temperatures on the Galveston beach range from 12.2°C (54°F) during the coldest month (January) to 28.5°C (83°F) during the warmest month (August). Likewise, mean water temperatures range from 11.8°C (53°F) in January to 30°C (86°F) in August. The mean salinity at Galveston is 29.1‰ (parts per thousand), but the recorded salinities have dropped as low as 3.2‰ and have risen as high as 39.2‰. This variability in the surface salinity results from the uneven distribution of the Gulf Coast's annual rainfall.

Organisms living between the tide marks may be exposed to different temperature regimes depending upon whether or not the tide is covering them. If they are exposed to the air, they may experience temperatures as low as −13°C (8°F) or as high as 38°C (101°F). However, if they are underwater, the temperature will probably be within the recorded range of 4°C (39°F) to 33°C (91°F).

The Fauna

The fauna of the northern Gulf of Mexico has three major elements: Carolinian, Caribbean, and cosmopolitan. It has great affinity with the fauna of the lower Atlantic Coast. Hence, zoogeographically this region is considered a disjunct segment of the Carolinian Province, which extends from Cape Hatteras, North Carolina, to southern Florida and across the northern Gulf of Mexico. These two regions were connected before the Florida peninsula was formed, permitting the migration of Atlantic species into the northern Gulf. Some species may have entered the Gulf later as the water temperatures of southern Florida were lowered to a level tolerable to northern species during the glacial ages. Today the Florida peninsula and the Florida Current, which flows out of the Gulf, discourage such migrations. Many of our best known species, such as the blue crab and the common oyster, are found on both coasts.

Faunas of the eastern and western portions of the northern Gulf of Mexico are separated at a major faunal transition near Desoto Canyon (Figure 1.1). This faunal change is apparently related to a change in substrate, from calcareous in the east to terrigenous in the west. Predominant sediments along the coasts of Alabama and northwestern Florida arise from fossil and recent coralline deposits and hence are marine in origin. Sediments to the west are predominately silts and siliceous sands arising from continental erosion and are transported to the Gulf by numerous rivers, the largest being the Mississippi River. These sediments differ in grain size, density, pore space, and organic content, and thus attract different species, particularly among those taxa that construct burrows or ingest sediment.

Another factor that contributes to this faunal difference is the Loop Current, which transports warm Caribbean water and entrained larvae of Caribbean species northward along the Florida coast. Thus, the eastern Gulf not only has a sediment type similar to that in the Caribbean, but also has access to a wide variety of tropical larvae. High turbidity of western Gulf waters discourages colonization by several taxa common in the eastern Gulf, such as sponges, reef-building corals, and algae.

Some of the Carolinian species have different life styles at the extremes of their geographical ranges. The common purple sea urchin spawns in summer in the northern portion of its range and in late winter in Texas. And the hermit crab, *Pagurus longicarpus*, migrates from shallow water into the deeper parts of the bays during the winter on the East Coast but migrates from deep water to the shallows during the winter in Texas. Several of these species also reach a larger size in the northern portion of their ranges than they do in the Gulf of Mexico.

The Caribbean or tropical element of the northwestern Gulf Coast fauna is generally a temporary one. It becomes established every few years when the local climate is sufficiently mild and largely disappears during severe winters. Most of these tropical species, such as the gorgonians, are most common south of 28°N latitude (Corpus Christi, Texas and St. Petersburg, Florida). These species generally arrive as planktonic larvae carried north along the coasts of Mexico and Florida or across the Gulf from Yucatan.

Cosmopolitan species (i.e. species found around the world) are often distributed by ships that visit Gulf Coast ports. Barnacles, hydroids, serpulid worms and other sessile species are common fouling organisms found on the hulls of ships. Crabs and isopods that can tolerate exposure to air often find crevices on ships, especially wooden ships, that are suitable niches for a transoceanic voyage. Mud crabs, flatworms, and amphipods are often transported from one part of the world to another in shipments of seed oysters. Other species, such as the Portuguese man-of-war and the by-the-wind sailor, are carried across the ocean via currents and wind.

Life Styles

The animals that inhabit the northern Gulf Coast have diverse means of making a living. Perhaps the most common method of obtaining food is filter-feeding, i.e. by straining microscopic plankton from the water. Most filter-feeders set up a current of water by beating thousands of tiny cilia. This current is driven through small pores lined with bristles and coated with mucous. The plankton becomes entangled in the mucous, which is periodically sloughed off to the mouth, where the food is sorted and ingested. Filter-feeding is commonly employed by clams, oysters, mussels, slipper limpets, sponges, and some worms. Variations are exhibited by barnacles, whose long, curved legs strain plankton from passing water, and by sea anemones and hydrozoans, whose tentacles are armed with cells designed to immobilize and grasp plankters that brush against them.

Another common feeding mode is deposit-feeding. Many crabs obtain food by shifting through the sediment for minute food particles that are removed by especially adapted mouthparts. Some worms are even more direct; the sediment is simply swallowed and the sorting is done chemically in the gut. Scavenging is a related mode of feeding employed by larger crabs and some other crustaceans, such as isopods and amphipods. Scavengers are opportunists, exploiting the corpses of other animals that sporadically become available for larger bits of food. Many scavengers are also deposit feeders or predators who are not adverse to picking up a bit of easy food.

Several animals on the jetties and in the salt marshes graze upon the algae which grows on the rocks and grass stalks. Limpets and littorine snails employ a radula, a thin, flexible band covered with numerous rows of teeth, which is rasped back and forth over the rock or plant surface to remove the microscopic algal film. Sea urchins and crabs eat larger algae, which can be grasped and torn from the rock.

Carnivorous snails exhibit various feeding modes. Some bore a hole through the shell of their prey with the radula, frequently aided by chemical secretions. Others pry open or chip away the prey's shell with the lip of their own shell. Shell-chipping is a technique also employed by predacious crabs when feeding on bivalves, snails and hermit crabs. Other crabs and

mantis shrimp are ambush predators, lying buried in the sand until a smaller animal wanders too near.

Invertebrate Taxa

Phylum Porifera

sponges

The sponge fauna of the northwestern Gulf of Mexico is not diverse, probably due to a combination of the cold winters and reduced salinities. Sponges are much more prevalent in the eastern Gulf, especially where coral reefs are found. Sponges common to the northwestern Gulf Coast are boring sponges, which may be found in snails, clam and oyster shells, or encrusting sponges inhabiting artificial reefs.

Phylum Cnidaria

jellyfish, anemones, coral

The cnidarians are a very common and diverse group, which includes the hydroids, jellyfish, sea anemones, sea pansies, gorgonians and stony corals. Cnidarians are unique in possessing nematocysts, with which they immobilize their prey. Hydroids may be found on almost any firm substrate—rocks, pilings, shells, boats, buoys, crabs and seaweeds. Although hydroids are very common, they are usually overlooked by the casual observer because they are small and look like plants. Jellyfish, or medusae, are generally much larger than hydroids, but they are difficult for the landlocked naturalist to see unless they wash up on the beach. Sea anemones are common on the jetties, where they are often disguised by a covering of shell fragments, and on oyster reefs and hermit crab shells. Sea pansies are found offshore on sandy bottoms. Although they occasionally wash ashore, they are most often observed in trawl samples. Gorgonians (sea whips and sea fans) may be found on the jetties below the water line or attached to rocks or large shells offshore. Stony corals generally prefer warmer water than is found on this coast during the winter. Well developed coral reefs may be found offshore at the Flower Gardens Bank, but only one species lives nearshore, on rocks or other solid objects.

Phylum Ctenophora

comb jellies

The ctenophores are a small group of medusa-like animals, commonly called comb-jellies, which often become very abundant in the bays. The eerie light of their bioluminescence is a common sight to flounder fishermen. Ctenophores can be recognized by their eight rows of cilia. The beating of these tiny cilia propels the ctenophore through the water and brings it into contact with its planktonic food. In contrast to the cnidarians, most ctenophores lack nematocysts but have tentacles with adhesive structures which trap plankters. Two species are found along the northwestern Gulf Coast, one predominates in summer and the other in winter.

Phylum Platyhelminthes

flatworms

The flatworms are small, secretive animals; thus they are easily overlooked. They have flattened, oval bodies and numerous eyes, often distributed in a band around the margin. Species peculiar to this area can be found on oyster reefs, in shells occupied by hermit crabs, on *Sargassum* and crawling over muddy sediments.

Phylum Rhynchocoela

proboscis worms

The nemerteans or proboscis worms are long, slender, fragile worms. The length of the proboscis in some species exceeds the length of the whole rest of the body. Everted by muscular contractions, it wraps around the prey and is then retracted, bringing the food to the mouth. The prey is usually swallowed whole, but if it is too large, its tissues are sucked out. Many nemerteans are very colorful, and some are patterned with bright stripes and bands. They may be found by straining mud or sand-mud through a sieve.

Phylum Annelida

round worms

The most common marine annelid worms are the polychaetes. The bodies of these worms are conspicuously divided into numerous segments, each of which is equipped with a pair of lateral appendages. These appendages, called parapodia, are modified according to the worm's life style. In tube-dwelling species the parapodia are greatly reduced; in burrowing species they are large, efficient locomotory devices. The sedentary species may be found attached to almost any solid object in the water, but they are most common on calcareous substrates such as shells. They may also be found in tubes or burrows in the mud. The errant species can be found by sifting through sediments or by carefully examining other animals, such as sea stars, sea pansies, hermit crabs and sea urchins, for commensal species.

Phylum Mollusca

oysters, snails, clams, octopus

The mollusks are a very large and diverse group which includes such familiar forms as snails, clams, oysters, chitons, squids and octopuses. Snails and bivalves are found in all nearshore environments and, being the object of many a collector's affection, are among the best known marine invertebrates. Chitons live on hard substrates such as oyster shells. Squids and octopuses are best known to shrimp fishermen, in whose trawls they are frequently caught.

Phylum Arthropoda

crabs, shrimp

This is the largest animal phylum, primarily because it includes the insects. There are very few marine insects, however, and the great majority of the marine arthropods belong to the Class Crustacea. The crustaceans include the barnacles, copepods, amphipods, isopods, crabs, shrimp and lobsters. Barnacles are among the more ubiquitous invertebrates in the sea; they are found on jetties, pilings, boat hulls, shells, crabs, turtles, whales, driftwood and *Sargassum*. Copepods are one of the most important invertebrate taxa in the sea, forming a major food link between the microscopic plant life called phytoplankton and small fish. Isopods and amphipods may be found in damp crevices, among the seaweeds on the jetties, in edible beach drift and in salt marshes. Various crabs may be found swimming in the bays, hiding among the boulders on the jetties, burrowing in the surf zone or living in old tin cans. Likewise, various species of shrimp live on the muddy bay bottom, crawl about on the jetty boulders, cling to submerged grasses or burrow into mud flat.

Phylum Echinodermata

sea stars, urchins

The echinoderms are generally large, benthic invertebrates such as the sea stars, brittle stars, sea urchins, sand dollars and sea cucumbers. Sea stars and brittle stars can be found on sandy or sandy-mud bottoms from the surf zone to deep water. Brittle stars are also found on oyster reefs. Commonly found on jetties, sea urchins may also live on sandy bottoms. Beds of sand dollars may be found in sandy sediments just beyond the surf zone or in the passes. Sea cucumbers are usually found on grass flats.

Phylum Bryozoa

moss animals

The bryozoans are small, colonial animals whose colonies have two growth forms. One form closely resembles a hydroid colony, and the other form ap-

pears as a thin encrustation covering the surface of a shell or rock. The latter form is more easily recognized and is common on shells inhabited by hermit crabs. The individuals within a colony may be modified for feeding, reproduction or protection. Each feeding individual is equipped with a crown of tentacles which sweeps food out of the passing water and toward the mouth.

Phylum Chaetognatha

arrow worms

The arrow worms are long, slender planktonic animals. They are equipped with lateral fins which aid in gliding through the water and with several pairs of long spines on the head which aid in food capture. They generally prefer saline water to brackish water but may occasionally be found in the bays when the salinity is high. They are voracious predators on plankters.

Phylum Chordata

sea squirts

A few of the chordates lack vertebrae, and hence are invertebrates. Among these are the sea squirts and the larvaceans. Sea squirts are round gelatinous animals with two short siphons projecting from the body. Water laden with planktonic food is drawn into one of these tubes, the food is digested and the water is forced out the other tube. They are sessile animals that can be found on oyster reefs, on pilings and on old shells. Larvaceans are peculiar planktonic animals that resemble small tadpoles in which the tail is attached at right angles to the head. They live in disposable gelatinous "houses" equipped with filters for straining food from the water.

Jetties and Groins

Rocky intertidal habitats along the northwestern Gulf Coast are limited to man-made jetties and groins designed to impede the movement of sand along the shore. Organisms living on these structures may be exposed to severe physical stresses from waves and currents. The more fragile animals must seek refuge in the crevices or on the leeward side of the boulders. Most of the animals on the jetties either filter plankton from the water, graze on algae or diatoms that grow on the rocks, or search for scraps of food left by the ebbing tide, gulls, or fishermen.

In spite of the paucity of rocky shore habitats on the Gulf Coast, those that do exist share common features with most other rocky shores around the world. These features include zones of ecologically similar organisms that adapt to similar regimes imposed by the tides and surface waves. On the tops of the jetties there may be a splash zone, wetted only by the spray of breaking waves. Below this lies a zone which is submerged during nearly all high tides and exposed during nearly all low tides: the littoral zone. Below that uncovered by the lowest tides, is the sublittoral zone. Some marine biologists also recognize supralittoral and infralittoral fringes, which are wetted only by extreme high tides or high waves and exposed only by extreme low tides, respectively.

The most common animals found in rocky shore habitats are the acorn barnacles, *Chthamalus fragilis* and *Balanus improvisus;* the zebra periwinkle, *Littorina lineolata;* the false limpet, *Siphonaria pectinata;* the rock louse, *Ligia exotica;* the hermit crab, *Clibanarius vittatus;* the stone crab, *Menippe mercenaria;* the procelain crab, *Petrolisthes armatus;* the drill, *Thais haemastoma;* and the warty sea anemone, *Bunodosoma cavernata.*

The Ubiquitous Barnacles

The fragile barnacle, *Chthamalus,* is the most common acorn barnacle at the higher levels on the jetties. It is generally small (about 0.5 cm), but its size and shape vary greatly depending upon its food supply and upon how crowded it is. Crowded barnacles are more elongate and thus are more easily broken off the rocks by waves than are the squatter uncrowded barnacles.

Three other acorn barnacles, *Balanus improvisus,* the ivory barnacle, *Balanus eburneus,* and the striped barnacle, *Balanus amphitrite amphitrite,* are often found on jetties, pilings, driftwood and shells. The acorn barnacles are distinguished by their shell structures, composed of a base, a wall consisting of six interlocking plates and an operculum consisting of four valves. The bases and walls of the shells of the northwestern Gulf Coast species of *Balanus* are calcareous and porous. The base of *Chthamalus'* shell is membraneous, and its wall is calcareous but solid. Moreover, the plates of the walls of these genera overlap differently (Figure 2.1).

Balanus eburneus is the largest acorn barnacle in this area. It can be distinguished from *Balanus improvisus* and *Balanus amphitrite* by the longitudinal grooves on the larger pair of opercular valves (called scuta) and the broad zone of overlap (the radius) between the plates (Figure 2.2). *Balanus amphitrite* also has broad radii, but lacks the longitudinally grooved scuta and is marked by thin gray or purple stripes (except in old, bleached shells). *Balanus improvisus* has narrow radii and no longitudinal grooves on the scuta.

Barnacles are filter-feeders, screening plankton from the water with their featherlike legs. These legs

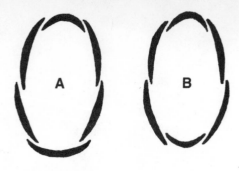

Figure 2.1 Configurations of shell wall plates for the acorn barnacles, *Balanus* (A) and *Chthamalus* (B).

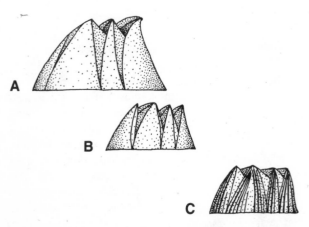

Figure 2.2 Lateral view of the acorn barnacles, *Balanus eburneus* (A), *Balanus improvisus* (B) and *Balanus amphitrite amphitrite* (C). (x 5)

are withdrawn behind the tightly closing opercular valves when the tide recedes. This keeps the barnacle moist for several hours. However, if the barnacle is not wetted by the returning tide or by the spray from a wave for a longer time it may perish. This places an upper limit on the portion of the jetty that is inhabitable by *Chthamalus*. A lower limit may be created through crowding by other barnacle species or through predation by *Thais haemastoma*. *Thais* is less tolerant of drying than is *Chthamalus*, thus the higher levels on the jetty provide *Chthamalus* with a refuge from this predator.

The dense aggregations of barnacles are caused in part by the affinity that barnacle larvae have for rock that is or has been occupied by other barnacles of the same species. A chemical substance in the shells of older barnacles attracts their young to settle nearby. This is critical to the barnacles since they must cross-fertilize even though they are sessile, have internal fertilization and are hermaphroditic (each individual produces both eggs and sperm). Only the eggs of bar-

nacles that settle close to one another can be fertilized. The fertilized egg hatches into a planktonic nauplius larva, which undergoes six molts and then develops into a second larva called a cypris. The planktonic stage of a barnacle's life usually lasts less than two weeks, but it may be prolonged if the cypris larva has difficulty locating a suitable habitat. The cypris larva uses a cement produced by special glands on its antennae to attach itself to the rock. Actually, a barnacle is an animal that spends its life standing on its head and capturing food with its feet.

The zebra periwinkle, *Littorina lineolata* (Figure 2.3), can usually be found among the barnacles. This black and white snail is so tiny that it is often found inside the shells of dead barnacles. *Littorina* scrapes algae and diatoms from the rock, often removing particles of rock in the process. Thus, it is a "bio-eroder" and is partially responsible for numerous depressions in soft rocks such as sandstones. It is often found aggregated in crevices, of its own making or not, which help protect it from pounding waves and drying wind.

Figure 2.3. The zebra periwinkle, *Littorina lineolata*. (x 5)

Another common grazer on the jetty is the false limpet, *Siphonaria pectinata* (Figure 2.4). Like barnacles, limpets have a conical shape that helps them resist the force of waves breaking over them. Like *Littorina*, *Siphonaria* grazes on microscopic algae and diatoms, and it often erodes a shallow depression into which its shell fits snugly. It is often camouflaged by filamentous algae that grow on its shell. This bio-eroder is quite destructive to soft beach rocks in southeastern Florida. Unlike most other marine snails, *Siphonaria* is a pulmonate gastropod, i.e. gases are exchanged across the lining of its mantle cavity

Figure 2.4. The false limpet, *Siphonaria pectinata*. (x 2)

rather than through a gill. Hence it is called a "false" limpet. These snails are hermaphroditic, thus two individuals may fertilize each other's eggs. The eggs are laid in yellow or yellow-green ribbons 3-4 cm long. These gelatinous egg ribbons are often laid in a semi-circle.

Fleet-footed Scavengers

Scurrying for shelter among the boulders, the isopod or rock louse, *Ligia exotica* (Figure 2.5), resembles a cockroach retreating from your approach. These fleet-footed scavengers, called sea slaters in England, migrate with the changing tide and thus are able to avoid many of the hazards of life in the intertidal zone. *Ligia* is most active near dusk or on overcast days; on warm sunny days it stays in the cooler crevices between the boulders. *Ligia* stays near the water and shuns the warming rays of the sun because its platelike gills dry out easily. When it finds itself exposed to the sun's heat, water from its permeable cuticle evaporates and cools the isopod, but it must withstand considerable concentration of its blood resulting from the water loss. *Ligia* can often be observed wetting its gills at the water's edge. Since its gills are located under its abdomen, it need only submerge the posterior portion of its body. It replaces lost internal water by drinking, either through its mouth, or more commonly, through its anus. Anal drinking is aided by dilation of the rectum and antiperistalsis, i.e. reversing the flow through the alimentary canal.

Ligia can change its color by concentrating or dispersing a dark pigment called melanin in special cells called chromatophores under its cuticle. When the melanin is concentrated, it appears as black dots that are so tiny as to be nearly invisible; thus the isopod as a whole seems pale. When the melanin is dispersed, the isopod seems dark gray. *Ligia* is usually found in its dark phase during the day and in its pale phase at night, except when influenced by a full moon or other bright light.

Unlike most other jetty invertebrates, *Ligia* does not have a planktonic larval stage. The young are kept in a brood pouch between their mother's legs until they are old enough to fend for themselves on the jetty. As many as 120 young may be carried by a single female. Although this number seems trivial compared to the many thousands or millions of eggs produced by a blue crab or an oyster, *Ligia's* young stand a better chance of survival because of their parental care.

A smaller isopod, *Sphaeroma quadridentatum* (Figure 2.6), can usually be found by searching carefully among the algae growing on the jetty or among the clusters of barnacles and littorines. Like its terrestrial relatives, the pillbugs, *Sphaeroma* will roll into a ball if threatened. It can often be found in this spherical form inside old barnacle shells. Unlike other American representatives of this genus, *Sphaeroma quadridentatum* lacks tubercles on its abdomen. Most members of this genus bore into wooden structures, and one species, *Sphaeroma terebrans,* is very destructive to the prop roots of red mangroves in southwestern Florida.

Figure 2.6. The smooth-backed *Sphaeroma, Sphaeroma quadridentatum.* (x 4)

Oyster Drills and Hermit Crabs

The drill or rock shell, *Thais haemastoma,* is a predator of barnacles and young oysters (spat) on the jetties. *Thais* is best known as an oyster predator found on oyster beds, but it is equally destructive to noncommercial species on rocky shores. Two varieties of this snail are found in Texas; some malacologists consider these the subspecies *Thais haemastoma floridana* and *Thais haemastoma canaliculata* (Figure 2.7). The latter is recognized most easily by the double row of large knobs on its shell and the numerous grooves on the inside of the lip. However, intermediate forms are common and there is serious doubt that these two forms deserve subspecies rank.

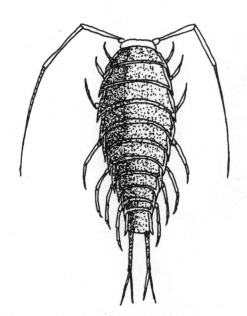

Figure 2.5. The rock louse, *Ligia exotica.* (x 2)

The shells of *Thais* are used by the striped hermit crab *Clibanarius vittatus,* which is commonly found at or near the water line along the jetty. *Clibanarius* (Figure 2.8) can also be found in the shells of several species of snails that live on sandy substrates offshore, primarily, the moon snail, *Polinices duplicatus,* and the whelks, *Busycon perversum pulleyi* and *Busycon spiratum.* Young *Thais* (approximately 1 cm long) are usually found riding on the shells of adults or on shells inhabited by hermit crabs. *Clibanarius* is a scavenger, feeding on a wide variety of items such as algae, the bodies of organisms that wash up on the rocks, and fishing bait. It disappears from the shallows around the jetty for two or three months during the winter. During this period it can usually be found in the channels adjacent to the jetties. There it aggregates and often buries itself in the sediment.

Clibanarius is occasionally burdened by the parasitic isopod, *Bopyrissa wolffi* (Figure 2.9), which resides in its host's gill chamber. It occurs primarily in young hermit crabs and is easily detected by a pronounced swelling of the crab's carapace over the isopod. Male *Bopyrissa* are much smaller than the females and thus more easily overlooked.

The shells of both snails and hermit crabs on the jetties are sometimes used as a substrate by the half-folded dove snail, *Anachis semiplicata* (Figure 2.10).

Figure 2.7. The rock shells, *Thais haemastoma canaliculata* (A) and *Thais haemastoma floridana* (B). (x 1)

Figure 2.8. The striped hermit crab, *Clibanarius vittatus,* in a barnacle encrusted *Busycon* shell. (x 1)

Figure 2.9. A female parasitic isopod, *Bopyrissa
wolffi* (x 15).

Figure 2.12. The warty sea anemone, *Bunodosoma cavernata*.
(x 1)

Anachis may also be found on shells on the mud flat
or on blades of shoal grass (*Halodule*) or turtle grass
(*Thalassia*). It attaches itself to the grass blade by a
thin mucous thread. This tiny carnivore is most conspicuous when it forms clusters of 10 or more individuals, possibly for breeding.

The cancellate cantharus, *Cantharus cancellarius*
(Figure 2.11), is another small snail that is often found
on the jetties or on the sand flats adjacent to the jetties. It resembles *Thais* but has a more textured shell
and rarely exceeds 3 cm in length. Its yellowish-brown
shell usually supports an algal flora when the snail is
alive. The tinted cantharus, *Pisania tincta,* may be
found on the jetties from Port Aransas south. It is
usually darker (blue-gray or chocolate brown) than
the cancellate cantharus.

Figure 2.10. The half-folded dove shell,
Anachis semiplicata. (x 3)

Figure 2.11. The cancellate cantharus, *Cantharus cancellarius*.
(x 1.5)

Flowers in the Crevices

During the low tides the anemone *Bunodosoma
cavernata* (Figure 2.12) is often exposed. Anemones
are difficult to recognize out of water, as they shrink
against the rock and fold in their tentacles. A more
rewarding view may be found by seeking an anemone
that is just below the waterline. Sea anemones are not
plants, as they appear, but are sessile animals. A
Bunodosoma on the jetty is usually light brown with
vertical rows of pale blue dots on the stalk. Its tentacles have a blue stripe on the side nearest the mouth
and are usually reddish on the opposite side. However,
individuals from other habitats are often much duller
in color than the jetty form.

Like most other anemones, *Bunodosoma* is capable
of crawling. However, its temporary attachment to the
rock is firm and it is often imbedded in a hole or
crevice, so that removing an anemone in one piece is
not a simple task. Some anemones, particularly those
in contact with waterborne sand and debris, capture
small fragments until they seem to have formed a shell
crust. This "crust" protects them from a variety of
hazards: desiccation, sunburn, abrasion from the sand
or attack by predators. Another jetty anemone,

Bunodactis texaensis, is very similar in appearance to *Bunodosoma,* and can only reliably be distinguished from it by a microscopic examination of the nematocysts. *Bunodactis* is usually light gray with dark gray streaks on the tentacles.

Figure 2.13. *Aiptasiomorpha texaensis.* (x 4)

A small pinkish anemone, *Aiptasiomorpha texaensis* (Figure 2.13), can be found near the far ends of the jetties on rocks that are exposed only during extreme low tides. It is only about 0.5 cm in diameter and is usually found in clusters. *Aiptasiomorpha* reproduces asexually by budding off tiny juveniles, which can occasionally be seen attached to their parent's stalk. When completely formed, these young anemones crawl off onto the substrate and colonize the area around the parent, forming a cluster, or clone, of genetically identical individuals. *Aiptasiomorpha* is tolerant of low salinities and is often found on oyster reefs as well as on jetties.

An anemone's nematocysts are long, barbed filaments that remain coiled inside cells on the tentacles until disturbed by contact with a potential food item, such as a fish or a finger. They then extend very rapidly into the food, and if it is small enough to be held by the nematocysts, the prey is passed by the tentacles to the mouth. Some nematocysts carry a toxin to weaken the prey. These nematocysts are not dangerous to humans, but they do provide a sticky sensation when the tentacles are touched. The anemone does not have an anus, so any undigestible portions of its prey must be ejected through the mouth.

Crabs and Shrimp on the Jetty

A close look into the pools between the boulders at low tide may reveal one or more stone crabs, *Menippe mercenaria* (Figure 2.14). *Menippe* is generally a scavenger on the jetties, depending upon the water currents and the fisherman who keep it supplied with

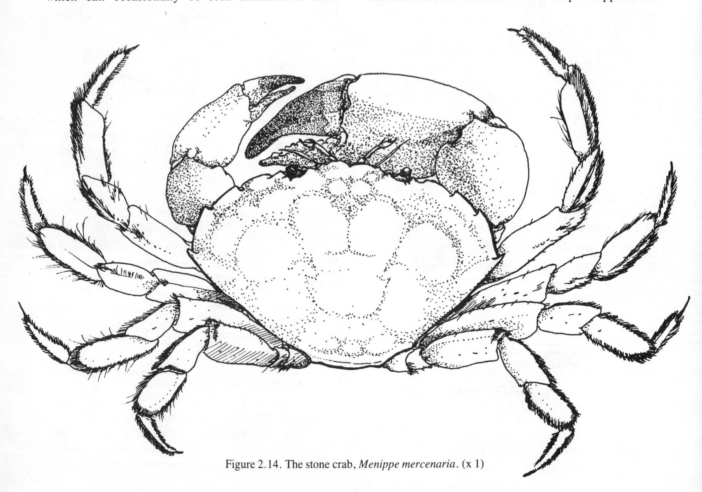

Figure 2.14. The stone crab, *Menippe mercenaria.* (x 1)

free food. In the absence of such easy prey it is quite capable of breaking open oyster spat or chipping away the shells of hermit crabs with its powerful claws. Fingers are no match for these claws either, so these crabs should be handled very carefully.

The porcelain crab, *Petrolisthes armatus* (Figure 2.15), may be found clinging to the bottoms of rocks in these pools. This small crab (3-4 cm) is aptly named, as it is extremely fragile. Its flattened claws are readily autotomized, or cast off, with a minimum of human handling. *Petrolisthes* is a filter feeder. It clings to the rock surface and alternatively waves its maxillipeds through the water above its head. These maxillipeds have a fringe of long setae which strain planktonic food from the water. Other mouthparts intermittently remove this food from the setae and transfer it to the mouth. *Petrolisthes* occasionally supplements its planktonic diet by scraping algae off rocks and shells or by scavenging dead animals that it is fortunate enough to come upon.

Figure 2.16. The peppermint shrimp, *Hippolysmata wurdemanni*. (x 2)

"cleaning shrimp," which remove parasites and infected tissue from the bodies of the fish. Cleaning shrimp often set up stations to which the fish come to be treated. Although this behavior has not been reported in the peppermint shrimp, it will pick at sores and hairs if permitted to crawl about on your hand. This annoying behavior is related to its probable habit of scavenging among the subtidal organisms encrusting the jetty.

Migration of the Sea Hare

Another sight familiar to visitors to the south Texas jetties in late Spring and early Summer is the migration of the sea hare, *Aplysia brasiliana* (Figure 2.17), as it passes through the channel on its way to breed in the grass flats of the bays. *Aplysia* is a benthic her-

Figure 2.15. The porcelain crab, *Petrolisthes armatus*. (x 2)

The persistent jetty explorer will be rewarded with a glimpse of the beautiful little peppermint shrimp, *Hippolysmata wurdemanni* (Figure 2.16). As its name suggests, this shrimp is translucent with delicate red stripes. The peppermint shrimp is most abundant near the tips of the southern jetties., where it resides deep in the crevices. *Hippolysmata* is closely related to the

Figure 2.17. The sea hare, *Aplysia brasiliana,* shown swimming. (x 0.6)

bivore that grazes on algae growing on the rocks. It is a surprisingly strong swimmer with the aid of a pair of large "wings." These wings which fold over the sea hare's back are actually extensions of the snail's foot. Although *Aplysia* appears shell-less, it has a very thin internal shell which lies over the hump of organs on the posterior of the animal. It is hermaphroditic and each individual may lay up to half a billion eggs in a tangled mass of yellow strings. *Aplysia* dies soon after its eggs are laid; it has a lift span of only one year. If molested, the sea hare releases a purple ink into the water.

Spiny Delicacies

The south Texas jetties are also the home of the sea urchin *Arbacia punctulata* (Figure 2.18). This purple urchin is also a herbivore who enjoys large, leafy seaweeds. Its long spines protect it from many potential predators, but it is still vulnerable to the crushing force of waves breaking against the jetties and to the strong jaws of some aggressive fishes. Hence it prefers to stay in the crevices and on the leeward side of the jetty. The sea urchin's gonads are eaten as a delicacy in many parts of the world. The shell of a sea urchin is called a test and the bumps represent the points where the spines were attached. The test is composed of fused calcareous plates, fitted together in a sturdy zigzag pattern.

The rows of tiny holes in the *Arbacia* test are openings for tube feet. These tube feet have a hollow core filled with seawater and a sucker at the tip. The urchin extends its feet by forcing more seawater into them until the sucker touches and attaches to the substrate. By contracting muscles in the tube feet, the urchin shortens them and pulls itself toward the point where the sucker is attached. By coordinating the movements of its tube feet, and with some help from the spines, the urchin is able to move quite easily across either horizontal or vertical surfaces. The spines on the top and bottom of the urchin are shorter than those around its equator, making it easier for the tube feet to reach the ground.

The two larger openings in the test are for the mouth and anus. The anus is located on the top side of the urchin, the mouth on the side nearest the substrate. The mouth contains an unusual chewing apparatus called the Aristotle's lantern. It consists of the housing and musculature for five long teeth, which meet at their tips to form a five-sided bite.

Arbacia is easily confused with another jetty urchin, *Echinometra lucunter*. Both species are approximately the same size and same color and are nearly equally abundant on South Texas jetties. However, they can be distinguished by close inspection of the plates surrounding the anal opening on the upper surface. In *Arbacia* these plates are four in number (sometimes three or five) and are sculptured with fine grooves in a reticulate pattern. In *Echinometra* there are numerous plates of various sizes with assorted bumps similar to those on which the spines pivot. Moreover, the spines around *Echinometra's* mouth have sharp tips, as opposed to the flattened tips of the oral spines in *Arbacia*.

Figure 2.18. The sea urchin, *Arabacia punctulata*. (x 1)

Figure 2.19. The tube-building amphipod, *Corophium louisianum*. (x 10)

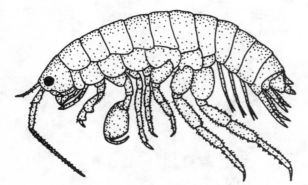

Figure 2.20. The beach flea, *Orchestia grillus*. (x 7)

Figure 2.21. The skeleton shrimp, *Caprella equilibra*. (x 8)

Beach Fleas and Skeleton Shrimp

The rocks on the sides of the jetties sometimes seem to be coated with a layer of slippery mud. On close inspection this mud is often found to contain thousands of tiny holes. These holes mark the burrows of the tube-building amphipod, *Corophium louisianum* (Figure 2.19). *Corophium* produces a sticky substance which it uses to reinforce the walls of its tube. It is a detritus feeder and will often make short forays from its burrow during high tide to search for food.

Another amphipod commonly found on the jetties is the beach flea, *Orchestia grillus* (Figure 2.20). *Orchestia* is larger than *Corophium,* but is still only about 0.5 cm long. It is most abundant when the green filamentous algae are especially lush on the jetty. Its green color helps to camouflage it in this setting. Should it be discovered, its powerful hind legs and curled abdomen act like a spring to propel it on a leap of up to 50 times its own length. *Orchestia's* legs are poor for supporting it, so it is usually seen lying or crawling on its side.

One of the most bizarre amphipods on the jetty is the so-called "skeleton shrimp," *Caprella equilibra* (Figure 2.21). Its long, slender body helps disguise it among the algal strands and hydroids to which it clings. *Caprella* is an ambush predator, lying in wait for an unsuspecting copepod, which it grabs with the claws on its second pair of legs. The smaller claws on its first legs then tear loose pieces of the prey and pass them to the mouth. *Caprella* is very sensitive to small water currents created by passing plankters. It may supplement its diet by scrapping the diatom-rich slime from the surface of the hydroid or grass to which it clings. *Caprella* has also been found on bryozoans, sea squirts, soft corals and the egg mass of the blue crab.

Jetty Animals That Resemble Plants

On the undersides of boulders and deep in the crevices, where direct sunlight seldom reaches, one frequently finds what appears to be brown or gray algae. On close inspection this "algae" is usually identifiable as one or more hydroid colonies. These hydroids also appear as a coarse fuzz on pieces of driftwood or *Sargassum* that wash up on the jetties. A hydroid colony typically consists of a flexible stem, which may be branched; several individuals called zooids attached to the stem; and a base by which the stem is attached to the substrate.

The zooids are polymorphic, i.e. several forms exist. The two most common forms are gastrozooids, which are feeding individuals, and gonozooids, which are reproductive individuals. The gastrozooids have a crown of nematocyst-bearing tentacles for food capture and resemble miniature anemones. The gonozooids typically consist of a stalk upon which several medusae are formed. In some species the medusae are released to become part of the plankton. The medusae produce gametes which are released into the sea. The fertilized egg develops into a larva called planula, which eventually settles to the bottom to become another hydroid colony.

A third type of zooid found in some species is the dactylozooid, which is a protective zooid usually resembling a long tentacle armed with nematocysts. Except for openings for the tentacles, the entire colony is surrounded by a chitinous covering called a perisarc.

Figure 2.22. The hydroid, *Bougainvillia in-aequallis*, with magnification of feeding and reproductive zooids. (x 10)

Figure 2.23. The hydroid, *Obelia dichotoma*, with magnification of feeding and reproductive zooids. (x 7)

Figure 2.24. The gorgonian, *Leptogorgia virgulata*, with galls formed over damaged area. (x 0.5)

Among the more common Texas jetty hydroids are *Bougainvillia inaequalis* (Figure 2.22) and *Obelia dichotoma* (Figure 2.23). *Bougainvillia* forms a large, heavy colony (to 10 cm high) with a very wrinkled perisac. *Obelia* is smaller (usually 1 to 1.5 cm high) and more delicate. Its perisarc is marked at nearly regular intervals by series of grooves, giving it an accordion-like appearance.

The gorgonian *Leptogorgia virgulata* (Figure 2.24) grows on the south Texas jetties. *Leptogorgia* is most accessible to divers as it is never found above the water level, even during low tides. Though it resembles a stringy seaweed, the gorgonian is a soft coral and its limbs are lined with minute polyps. It exists in two color phases: yellow and reddish purple. *Leptogorgia* hosts a small parasitic snail, *Simnialena uniplicata*. The shell of *Simnialena* is long and slender, so it has a low profile as it crawls along the gorgonian's branches. It also has two color phases which match those of its host.

Leptogorgia typically grows as a fan-shaped colony oriented perpendicular to the prevailing tidal currents, enabling it to maximize its catch of drifting food. The colony is supported by a horny axial rod, which is sufficiently flexible to permit the colony to bend in response to wave surge or strong currents, as a sapling bows to the wind. Additional support for the polyps and resistance to abrasion is obtained from a loose skeleton of calcareous spicules. These ornate spicules (Figure 8.5) can be easily observed under a microscope after dissolving the tissue in a solution of sodium hypoclorite (Clorox).

The stony corals which construct massive reefs in tropical seas are intolerant of the cold winters along the northern Gulf Coast. Such reefs may be found on salt domes on the continental shelf but are not found in shallow water nearshore. Only one stony coral, *Astrangia astreiformis* (Figure 2.25), lives in shallow water along the northwestern Gulf Coast. It is a colonial coral consisting of a few to several dozen polyps, each about 5-6 mm in diameter and connected to a common base. Pieces of coral skeleton are often found among shells cast up on the beach, and living colonies can be found on rocks and debris dredged from the bottom near the jetties. Colonies probably live on the jetties below the low tide level. The polyps are anemonelike and white or pale pink in color. Unlike anemones, they grow in tight clusters and are supported by an intricate calcareous skeleton. As the *Astrangia* colony grows, new polyps are added by fission, i.e. the division of an old polyp into two new polyps; or budding, i.e. the formation of a new (smaller) polyp as a bud off of an old polyp.

Figure 2.26. The fanworm, *Hypsicomus elegans,* expanded (left) and withdrawn (right). (x 7)

The fanworm *Hypsicomus elegans* (Figure 2.26) may also be found on shells or rocks dredged from the bottom adjacent to the jetties. Although its color is variable, it usually has a deep purple body and frequently has purple and white banded radioles. *Hypsicomus* constructs a tube from mucous and sand grains, which usually extends into a shell or calcareous rock. When disturbed the fanworm withdraws into its tube and the tip of the tube often rolls up, sealing the aperture.

The jetties along the South Texas Coast are the haunt of the Antillean nerite, *Nerita fulgurans* (Figure 2.27). This oddly shaped snail has a flattened spire and a very large aperture, which is rapidly constricted to a relatively narrow slit inside the lip. *Nerita* is a grazer found near the high tide level on jetty rocks and pilings. It has a tightly fitting operculum which enables it to withstand long periods out of the water.

Figure 2.25. The stony coral, *Astrangia astreiformis* (x 3)

Figure 2.27. The Antillean nerite, *Nerita fulgurans*. (x 2)

Sandy Beaches

Pounding surf, abrasive sand, and alternate periods of wetness and dryness of the sand beach present a harsh environment to organisms. Organisms in other environments must also deal with some of these factors, but on a sandy beach there is no solid substrate. There is nothing to hold on to in order to prevent one from being jostled about by wave action or washed in and out by the tide. The only refuge is within the sand. Consequently, most animals, except those that can swim well or crawl rapidly, burrow in the sand. Since many intertidal animals are concealed by their burrowing habit, a good clue to the abundance of the fauna in a particular area is the presence of feeding shore birds such as sandpipers, sanderlings and godwits.

Beach sand is composed of grains of various sizes and shapes. Although sand may be coarser or finer in different areas of the beach due to wave action, the space between the grains (pore space) is constant, averaging about 20% of the total volume. The pore space, which is determined by the degree of particle packing, affects the water level within the sand. This level is highest in fine sand. The capillary action allows for the maintenance of water in the sand above sea level. Sand above the water level is damp due to the adhesion of water to the sand particles and the presence of water vapor in the interstitial spaces. Thus a burrowing intertidal animal is in little danger of drying out at low tide. The presence of a water table in the sand is also important to animals living further back from the surf. By burrowing, they too can reach damp sand to protect themselves from desiccation.

In addition to protecting organisms against desiccation, a sand beach provides protection against temperature and salinity changes. Even a few millimeters of sand will protect against the hazards of insolation, i.e. exposure to the sun's rays. An animal that can burrow a few centimeters into the sand can survive in-

tolerable surface temperatures. Salinity is relatively constant a few centimeters beneath the surface, enabling an organism to survive a period of runoff after a rain or a drought.

A phenomenon called thixotropy is another physical aspect of sand that is important to burrowing animals. Thixotropy, strictly defined, is the ability of a gel to become liquid when stirred. Seemingly solid wet sand in the surf zone will "liquify" if agitated slightly. The burrowing movements of an animal are sufficient agitation to loosen the sand and allow an animal to dig in quickly.

On the other hand, sand is moved about by wave action putting animals that do not burrow deeply in constant danger of being washed out. The few animals who make permanent burrows in the surf zone must strengthen them by actually building tubes or strengthening the sand with mucous. Those animals who do not make permanent burrows, but move constantly through the sand, are generally streamlined and smooth-surfaced. Such form permits faster and easier burrowing.

Life on the Upper Beach

Having considered some of the factors that affect the inhabitants of sandy beaches, let's look at the animals and their adaptations concerning these factors. Like the jetties, the beach can be partitioned into supralittoral, littoral or intertidal, and sublittoral zones (Figure 3.1). The supralittoral zone begins at the base of the dunes and extends to the high tide line. One of the most conspicuous signs of animal life along the dunes is the rather large burrow of the ghost crab, *Ocypode quadrata* (Figure 3.2). This crab is active early in the morning, at dusk and at night, but usually remains in its burrow during the heat of the day. The depth of the burrow depends upon the water level

high tide

low tide

DRIFT
LINE

BEACH
FACE

LONGSHORE
BAR

LONGSHORE
TROUGH

Figure 3.1. Profile of a sandy beach.

within the sand, so it is wise to think twice before attempting to dig up a crab living at the base of the dunes. Its burrow may be as deep as 1.3 m (4 ft.) and may have a second entrance. The smaller crabs tend to live a little closer to the water, and consequently their burrows are shallower.

Ocypode is active from March through mid-December. During the colder months of the year, it plugs its burrow entrance with packed sand and remains dormant. Those females which were spawned early in the previous summer mature and ovulate once in April and again in August. In the following year, they may or may not ovulate and usually do not survive a third winter. Mating probably occurs through-out the year, and unlike the blue crab, *Callinectes, Ocypode* mates even when the female's integument is hard. Therefore, females can mate anytime after puberty. The female carries the eggs beneath her body and releases the developed larvae in the surf.

The ghost crab is a predator whose diet consists largely of mole crabs and bean clams, but it is also an opportunist. *Ocypode* will consume dead fish and the remains of animals found in beach debris, including stranded Portuguese men-of-war, *Physalia physalis,* which may be dragged to the burrow entrance. *Ocypode* is common in the surf at night since it must periodically exchange the seawater carried in its gill chamber. Its special adaptations to the supralittoral

Figure 3.2. The ghost crab, *Ocypode quadrata.* (x 1)

Figure 3.3. The tiger beetles, *Cicindela ocellata* (A), *Cicindela hamata* (B) and *Cicindela severa* (C). (x 2)

zone include thick setae around the openings to its gill chambers which keep sand out and reduce water loss. Desiccation is also reduced by *Ocypode's* relatively impermeable integument. It also has long antennae which can be flicked over its eyes to clear them of sand. These crabs interact socially with one another, communicating their intentions by the position of their chelae and by their body posture.

The tiger beetles, genus *Cicindela* (Figure 3.3), are another common, though often overlooked, resident of the upper shore and dunes. These small, fast-moving predators are characteristic of open, saline habitats such as beaches, mud flats, and the edges of salt marshes. More than 30 species are known from the northwestern Gulf Coast. They range in color from white to dark brown. They can be most easily recognized in the field by their behavior; when approached, they first run rapidly along the ground and then fly for a short distance if you get too close.

Life on the Littoral Beach

The intertidal zone is inhabited by some interesting animals, to which most of the discussion of physical factors applies. One of the most common animals here is the coquina or bean clam, *Donax variabilis roemeri* (Figure 3.4), which, as its name implies, comes in a variety of colors. Another species, *Donax texasiana,* is also fairly common and is usually uniform in color, in contrast to the rayed coloration of *Donax variabilis.*

During the spring, these species are found together at the water's edge; in the summer, only *Donax variabilis* is found in the intertidal zone. *Donax texasiana* moves into the shallow sublittoral zone. During the winter it is joined by *Donax variabilis* which is distinguished from *Donax texasiana* by the overlap of the latter's valves and the uniformity of the ventral teeth along its valve margins.

Donax is known to move up and down the beach slope with high and low tide, respectively. This migration is cued by vibrations in the sand produced by the pounding waves. Its adaptations for life in the surf zone include a large foot and a smooth streamlined shell, which enables it to burrow quickly into the sand. This little clam has short siphons which require it to stay near the sediment surface. This enables the filamentous alga, *Enteromorpha flexuosa,* to attach to the posterior ends of larger individuals. *Donax* is eaten by a variety of animals, including plovers and sander-

Figure 3.4. The bean clam, *Donax variabilis roemeri,* with siphons and foot extended. (x 2)

Figure 3.5. The mole crab, *Emerita portoricensis*. (x 1.5)

posterior end first. Its antennules are periodically cleaned of adhering sand grains by flicking them across a special set of curved setae on the antennae. The *Emerita* that are commonly encountered are females. The males are much smaller than the females, and when mature they locate a female and inconspicuously cling to her body. The bright orange eggs are laid in late spring and are brooded beneath the female's abdomen until they hatch. The planktonic larvae are dispersed by ocean currents to other beaches, and the less fortunate ones are carried far from shore, where they perish. The larvae undergo a series of molts, during which the structures required in adult life are acquired, and settle to the bottom to begin their lives in the surf zone. Another little crab, *Lepidopa websteri* (Figure 3.6), shares the surf zone with *Emerita*. This square-shaped crab also digs itself in backwards. Note its long, brushy antennules which act as "straws" in bringing water from the surface.

lings, drum, various crabs and the moon snail, *Polinices duplicatus*. The gonads of large *Donax* are frequently parasitized by the larval stages of flukes, which either severely impairs or prohibits reproduction. In uninfected individuals, reproduction apparently occurs in the spring and summer and the recruitment of young is greatest in May and October. These young overwinter and then mature, reproduce, and die in the ensuing year. Their growth is greatest in the fall and winter and lowest in the summer, when energy is shunted into reproduction rather than into growth.

Another inhabitant of the surf zone, the mole crab *Emerita portoricensis* (Figure 3.5), is also gregarious. This small, cylindrical-shaped crab is covered dorsally by a very smooth carapace. It has short, stout legs and a long, blade-like telson which is held flexed beneath the body. The quick strokes of its legs and the shovel-like action of the telson enable it to burrow quickly,

Snails That Leave Trails

Two snails are common in the intertidal zone. Both the lettered olive, *Oliva sayana* (Figure 3.7), and the moon snail, *Polinices duplicatus,* are predacious. These snails glide along just beneath the surface of the sand at a depth determined by the lengths of their siphons. As they push the sand around their shells they leave a furrow behind them which the knowledgeable collector can follow to locate the snail. Each has a large foot with the front portion (the propodium) modified for efficient burrowing. *Oliva* moves by extending the foot and then pulling the shell forward. Its golden-patterned mantle almost completely covers the shell when it is expanded. This probably reduces friction with the sand during movement and protects the shell from abrasion. The shell of this snail is very highly polished and cylindrical in shape—further adaptations for the sandy beach environment.

Oliva preys on *Donax* and other small smooth-surfaced clams, which it presumably smothers with its

Figure 3.6. *Lepidopa websteri*. (x 3)

Figure 3.7. The lettered olive, *Oliva sayana,* with siphon, tentacles and foot extended. (x 1.5)

Figure 3.8. The common Atlantic slipper shell, *Crepidula fornicata*, attached to the shell of *Oliva sayana*. (x 3.5)

foot. Its eggs are laid on the surface of the sand in transparent capsules containing from 20 to 50 eggs which develop into veliger larvae within a week. These veligers break out of the capsule and assume a planktonic existence until metamorphosing into the adult form.

The common Atlantic slipper shell, *Crepidula fornicata* (Figure 3.8), frequently washes ashore attached to an old *Oliva* shell or another suitable substrate, including another *Crepidula*. This slipper shell often lives in piles or chains as a result of its tendency to attach to the shells of each other. The largest and oldest members in a chain are females, the smaller and most recent arrivals are males. A hormone secreted by the females causes the upper individuals to remain males. As the lower females die, the males change sex and replace them. *Crepidula* is a filter-feeding snail. A coarse mucous web secreted across the entrance to the mantle cavity prevents large particles from entering the inhalant stream of water that flows over the gills. These large particles are trapped in the mucous and sloughed off as pseudofeces. Smaller particles which enter the mantle cavity are filtered out by the gills and passed to the mouth in mucous strings. An increase in water turbidity decreases the rate of growth, since

much energy is spent in preventing fouling of the mantle cavity. Under good conditions, *Crepidula* can increase up to 6 mm in length in three weeks. The inner shelf of *Crepidula* shells support the internal organs and is overlaid by the circular foot. Attachment to the substrate is maintained by the foot's suction. Seventy to one hundred eggs are laid in each of several thin-walled capsules attached to the substrate. The young emerge from these capsules as veliger larvae.

Polinices (Figure 3.9) is a voracious predator of clams, its favorites being *Donax* and *Dosinia,* though it is a cannibal when other prey are not available. It holds the clam or snail within the folds of its foot and drills a hole through the shell with its radula. The radula is supported by a structure called an odontophore. As muscles pull the radula back and forth over the odontophore, the whole apparatus is rotated and a round hole is gradually rasped through the shell of the victim. When the hole is complete, *Polinices* inserts its tubular proboscis and eats the meat inside. If you examine beached shells, you will find many that have been bored by *Polinices*. Its work is identified by the countersunk hole left in the shell of its prey.

Another gastropod which can sometimes be found in the surf zone is the auger shell, *Hastula salleana*

Figure 3.9. The moon snail, *Polinices duplicatus,* with siphon, tentacles and foot extended. (x 1)

(Figure 3.10). This bluish-gray to brown shell is shaped like an awl. Little is known of the habits of this species. It has been supposed that these snails prey on marine worms, although they may be carnivorous scavengers. *Hastula* has a large foot which is used to plow through the sand. The foot is also expanded to serve as a "sail," which carries the snail into deeper water with receding waves. This behavior is most pronounced during ebbing tides and keeps the auger from being stranded during low tide.

A common inhabitant of the shells of *Polinices, Oliva* and *Hastula* after the snail's death is the hermit crab *Isocheles wurdemanni* (Figure 3.11). This hermit crab is distinguished from *Pagurus* and *Clibanarius* by its very setose ("hairy") antennae, its small equal-sized claws and its small eyes. *Isocheles* scavenges in shallow water for edible matter and, like other hermit crabs, is always on the lookout for a more suitable shell. Unlike *Pagurus, Isocheles* appears to be confined to the surf beach.

Figure 3.10. The auger shell, *Hastula salleana.* (x 2)

Figure 3.11. The hermit crab, *Isocheles wurdemanni,* in a bryozoan encrusted shell. (x 1)

Worms in the Surf Zone

The tube-building worm, *Diopatra cupraea* (Figure 3.12), is a common inhabitant of the sandy subtidal zone and is sometimes found intertidally. Its tubes, usually vacant, are often washed ashore during storms. The end of the tube extends three to four centimeters above the surface of the sand and is camouflaged and reinforced with small shells, fragments of shells and bits of seaweed. The tube extends a foot or more beneath the sand and thus is firmly anchored. This tube is constructed of mucous secreted by glands in the worm's parapodia. Upon contact with sea water, the mucous hardens to a parchment-like material.

As the worm grows, the tube is enlarged by cutting a slit down the length of the tube, spreading the sides apart and adding a patch to the gap. The reinforced chimney may simply be cut away, discarded and constructed anew. *Diopatra* is a scavenger who captures bits of food that are washed near its tube or small animals that are attracted to the tube. It does not usually leave its tube entirely; however, in calm water it may make a quick sortie after a tasty meal lying just out of reach. The worm itself is quite handsome. Its reddish-brown body is iridescent and on each side of the head are bright red gills. Attempts to dig this animal up are frequently unsuccessful, as it simply escapes through the bottom of the tube.

Onuphis eremita oculata (Figure 3.13) is another tube-building polychaete living along the beach. It is a very long, slender worm that constructs a thin membranous tube covered by a layer of fine sand grains. The worm is usually reddish in color due to the presence of large blood vessels near the surface. It can be captured by straining sand from the surf zone or from farther offshore through a sieve. Unfortunately it is a very fragile worm and so is difficult to collect in one piece.

Figure 3.12. Two tube-building worms, *Diopatra cupraea.* The vertical tube is in its natural position; another worm is slightly extended from the exposed tube in which the unreinforced portion of the tube is also visible. (x 2)

Figure 3.13. The anterior portion of the polychaete *Onuphis eremita oculata*. (x 8)

Life Below the Littoral Zone

If we venture into the subtidal zone and wade to about the second or third sandbar, we may find clusters of the sand dollar, *Mellita quinquiesperforata* (Figure 3.14). It prefers habitats where the salinity is usually greater than 23‰; hence it is most common in the Gulf or in inlet-influenced areas in the bays. It also prefers a clean sandy substrate since it has difficulty burrowing in other sediments.

Sand dollars are closely related to sea urchins. Their skeletons are the waferlike tests so well known to beachcombers. While alive, their bodies are covered by numerous short spines which are used for locomotion as well as for protection. Both the mouth and the

Figure 3.14. Dorsal view of a live five-lunuled sand dollar, *Mellita quinquiesperforata*. (x 1)

anus are located on the bottom (flat) surface. Potential food particles are removed from the sediment by hundreds of tiny podia and moved to the mouth with the aid of mucous and cilia. *Mellita quinquiesperforata* has five oval holes or lunules through its test. The function of these holes is not clearly understood.

Mellita is very gregarious, a habit that is advantageous during its breeding season in the late spring and summer. The gametes are shed into the seawater and depend upon the proximity of the adults and the synchrony with which the gametes are shed for fertilization to occur. The fertilized ova develop into planktonic larvae that spend 4-6 weeks adrift. Young sand dollars ingest sand and store it in part of the gut as a "weight belt" to help hold them on the bottom.

The Scotch bonnet, *Phalium granulatum* (Figure 3.15), preys on *Mellita* and sea urchins. This orange and cream colored snail bores holes approximately 2 mm in diameter through the test of *Mellita* and inserts its radula to rasp out the edible material. *Phalium* is fairly abundant offshore though unbroken shells are seldom washed ashore. *Phalium* lays its eggs in capsules which are cemented together into a tower.

Figure 3.15. The Scotch bonnet, *Phalium granulatum*. (x 1)

Starfishes and Sea Pansies

Two sea stars, *Luidia clathrata* and *Luidia alternata* (Figure 3.16), are common along the beach and are occasionally caught in seines or with bait while crabbing. *Luidia clathrata* is uniformly cream or flesh colored, while *Luidia alternata* has dark brown bands alternating with a cream colored background on the arms. These are relatively large sea stars, 20-25 cm in diameter, with fairly slender arms. They prey on other echinoderms, especially brittle stars, but they will also

Figure 3.16. The banded sea star, *Luidia alternata.* (x 0.3)

Figure 3.18. The sea pansy, *Renilla mulleri* with expanded polyps. (x 1.5)

Figure 3.17. The sea star, *Astropecten duplicatus.* (x 0.3)

consume dead bait thrown overboard by fishermen. Their tube feet (or podia) lack the suckers used by many rocky shore sea stars to open bivalves. Thus, they swallow their food whole and regurgitate the undigestable parts. This can be a hazard as at least one *Luidia* is reported to have died after swallowing a whole sand dollar. Close inspection of the grooves on the underside of the sea star's arms may reveal one or more scaleworms, *Lepidonotus sublevis.* These short, fat worms are also commensal with hermit crabs and sea pansies.

A smaller sea star, *Astropecten duplicatus* (Figure 3.17), is more common than *Luidia* in deep water. This species is often caught in trawls on the shrimping grounds. It can be readily distinguished from *Luidia* by the rows of large plates along the sides of its arms. Like *Luidia, Astropecten* lacks suckers on its podia and must swallow its prey whole.

The reddish-purple sea pansy, *Renilla mulleri* (Figure 3.18), is one of the most fascinating sublittoral invertebrates. It consists of a flattened disk, upon which numerous polyps are located, and a stalk or peduncle which anchors it in the sediment. Like the related corals and gorgonians, *Renilla* is a colony of zooids. The longest polyps are feeding zooids, which capture small animals in their eight featherlike tentacles. The shore, stuby polyps are responsible for maintaining a flow of water through the disk, which circulates respiratory gases and helps to keep the disk inflated.

Renilla is well adapted for living in turbulent water. Its anchoring peduncle can be inflated and deflated independently of its disk, enabling it to inflate its buried peduncle while minimizing its resistance to currents by deflating its disk. Under more moderate conditions, it can increase its feeding surface up to 25 percent by inflating the disk. Small individuals can hold on in more turbulent water, i.e. closer to the surf, than large individuals, providing them greater protection from predators. *Renilla's* enemies include the sea star *Astropecten,* from which it defends itself by expanding its polyps to bring its nematocysts into play or by raising one edge of its disk such that the current carries it to safer ground. *Renilla* is a suspension feeder whose diet consists largely of small crustaceans and unicellular algae.

Yellow and Purple Whips

The sea whip, *Leptogorgia setacea* (Figure 3.19), is sometimes washed ashore in great tangled masses. This gorgonian attaches to shell fragments or other solid objects by a tuft of stolons, in contrast to the jetty species, *Leptogorgia virgulata,* which attaches by a

skeleton to which the polyps are attached. This
skeleton may be either yellow or reddish purple,
although the yellow form seems to be more common
in this area. The polyps can be partially retracted during unfavorable conditions. *Leptogorgia setacea* hosts
the snail, *Simnialena uniplicata* (Figure 3.19), which
grazes on the gorgonian's polyps. Male *Simnialena*
maintain territories; the female lays her eggs on the
sea whip in clumps of capsules, each containing many
eggs. *Simnialena* comes in yellow or purple usually
matching the color of its host. Its color is probably
due to its diet rather than to a genetic trait.

Life Beyond the Breakers

Crabs

The calico crab, *Hepatus epheliticus* (Figure 3.20),
lives offshore in shallow water. This brightly colored
crab can be recognized by the red patches on its gray
to pale yellow carapace and by its heavy claws. Berried females have been found in July; thus, this crab
reproduces in summer. The sea anenome, *Calliactis
tricolor,* is often found on *Hepatus'* back.

Another offshore crab, rarely found in the beach
drift, is *Calappa sulcata* (Figure 3.21). This crab preys
on hermit crabs and gastropods, such as the tulip
shells *Fasciolaria* spp., by chipping the shell with its
chela. The chela has a large tooth on its movable
finger and two large teeth on its immovable finger
which fit together such that when the lip of a shell is
held between them, a chip is easily broken off. The
shell is chipped successively until the animal inside is
exposed, drawn out and eaten. This modified claw is
one of the most refined shell opening mechanisms
found in the crustaceans. *Calappa* can be recognized
by its boxlike ovate shape and its heavy claws.

The giant red hermit crab, *Petrochirus diogenes*
(Figure 3.22), a common offshore species, is probably
a frequent prey of *Calappa*. It is found on mud, shell
and sandy bottoms in large shells, such as those of
Murex, Busycon and *Fasciolaria. Petrochirus* is the
largest hermit crab of the northwestern Gulf Coast
and carries a number of commensals, the most notable

Figure 3.19. The sea whip, *Leptogorgia setacea* attached to a
large *Laevicardium* shell with magnification of the parasitic
snail *Simnialena uniplicata.* (x 1)

basal plate. An uprooted *Leptogorgia setacea* may
survive for several weeks if it is not washed into the
surf zone and beached. Beach-washed specimens may
be abraded down to the axial rod, which looks like a
dark brown wire. During the sea whip's life this rod is
surrounded by an epithelium which secretes the

Figure 3.20. The calico crab, *Hepatus epheliticus.* (x 0.8)

Figure 3.21. The crab, *Calappa sulcata*. (x 1)

Figure 3.22. The giant red hermit crab, *Petrochirus diogenes*, emerging from the shell of a horse conch, *Pleuroploca gigantea*. (x 0.7)

Figure 3.23. The porcellanid crab, *Porcellana sayana*, with fringes of setae on its claws. (x 2)

Snails

The giant eastern murex, *Murex fulvescens* (Figure 3.24), is common just offshore and in the sand adjacent to the jetties. It can open oysters by pulling the valves apart with its large muscular foot, which is capable of exerting a pull of 7-10 kilograms. It also opens mussels and clams by chipping the prey shell with its own shell until it makes an opening large enough for its proboscis to enter. After feeding, *Murex* burrows into the sand and remains relatively stationary. During this time, new shell may be secreted. During the process of shell growth, the base of the spines around the lips is chemically dissolved. New shell is deposited and a new ridge of spines is

of which is the porcellanid crab, *Porcellana sayana* (Figure 3.23). Like its host, *Porcellana* is reddish in color. It is a small crab with a fringe of long hairs on the outer edges of its claws.

Figure 3.24. The giant eastern murex, *Murex fulvescens*. (x 0.7)

formed at the edge of the lip. The ridges of spines, or varices, around the shell represent former positions of the shell lip. Removal of the spines and formation of a new varix takes about ten days. *Murex* lays its eggs in small capsules, which are attached in protected areas under rocks.

The banded tulip, *Fasciolaria lilium* (Figure 3.25), is also a sublittoral predacious snail. Its smooth shell is mottled with reddish brown on a cream background and banded with thin brown spiral bands. The animal itself is flame red. These snails prey on a variety of organisms. *Fasciolaria* does not drill, but apparently pirates clams, such as *Chione* and *Mercenaria*, that have been drilled by other snails. It also chips the lips of small bivalves, including young oysters, but in this time-consuming process it often damages its own shell, indicating that this mode of attack is rather inefficient. *Diopatra* and *Onuphis* worms are also included in its diet, but considering the lengths of the tubes of these worms, successful attack probably depends a great deal on surprise. *Fasciolaria* eats these polychaetes by extending its proboscis down the tube and rasping away the worm's flesh with its radula. Small gastropods, including its own species and young *Murex*, are also consumed; however, only snails smaller than the attacking *Fasciolaria* are successfully attacked. Carrion is sometimes eaten in the absence of other food.

Fasciolaria deposits its eggs in flattened cornucopia-like capsules. Several dozen eggs are deposited in each capsule, but some are not fertilized and serve as "nurse" eggs which are eaten by the developing snails.

Figure 3.26. Tollin's wentletrap, *Epitonium tollina* (x 2).

Approximately a month after the eggs are deposited, the young emerge from the capsules as diminutive adults.

Tollin's wentletrap, *Epitonium tollini* (Figure 3.26), is a small predacious gastropod that lives along the sandy beach and in inlet-influenced areas in the bays. Wentletrap is a Dutch word meaning "spiral staircase" and refers to the numerous high ridges or varices ("stairs") on the shell. These varices originate as thickenings of the shell growth. *Epitonium* discharges a purple fluid when disturbed.

The Atlantic distorsio, *Distorsio clathrata* (Figure 3.27), lives on sandy bottoms from just beyond the surf zone to a depth of about 60 m. It is named for its very distorted shell aperture, which overlaps much of the ventral surface of the body whorl. This shell is often washed ashore on southern beaches during storms.

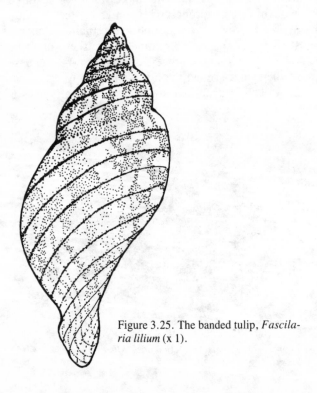

Figure 3.25. The banded tulip, *Fascilaria lilium* (x 1).

Figure 3.27. The Atlantic distorsio, *Distorsio clathrata* (x 1.5).

Figure 3.28. The giant cockle, *Laevicardium robustum*. (x 0.7)

Clams

A number of bivalves are common offshore. The giant cockle, *Laevicardium robustum* (Figure 3.28), is quite abundant. The large muscular foot of this cockle is dark red; its shell is mottled with deep red, brown and cream. It thrusts this foot against the sand, to move itself in a series of rolls and leaps. Its siphons are rather short and adorned with small, fleshy projections which prevent sand and large particles from entering the mantle cavity.

The ark clam family, Arcidae, has many representatives along the northwestern Gulf Coast. Perhaps the most common is the incongruous ark, *Anadara brasiliana* (Figure 3.29). This clam has unequal valves; the left overlaps the right valve when closed. The blood ark, *Anadara ovalis* (Figure 3.30), is also common. Unlike the former, it has a heavy dark brown periostracum (an organic covering which camouflages and protects the shell). The young of both of these species attach themselves to the substrate with a byssus, but they lose the byssus as they mature.

The ponderous ark, *Noetia ponderosa* (Figure 3.31), has a heavier shell and is characterized by the lack of a byssus in the adult and the presence of a heavy periostracum. The siphons of these filter-feeders are greatly reduced, and thus, they are shallow burrowers. The shallow burrowing habit and shifting sand during storms account for the great numbers of these clams we see on the beach after a storm. Members of this family can be immediately recognized by the hinge teeth on the valves. The tooth structure, called ctenodont, consists of a number of vertical grooves across the hinge line. These identical, comblike teeth constitute a primitive trait, as does the equal size of the anterior and posterior muscles which close the shell.

The pen shells, *Atrina seminuda* and *Atrina serrata* (Figure 3.32), also live offshore in muddy-sand or sandy substrate. These olive brown wedge-shaped clams spin a heavy byssus which helps anchor them, pointed end down, in the substrate. Once the clam is uprooted its chances or reestablishing itself are small since the foot is quite reduced. This animal exhibits an anisomyarian muscle structure, in that the anterior adductor muscle is very small and the posterior adductor muscle is quite large. This is an adaptation related to its orientation in the substrate. These clams harbor commensal crabs of the genus *Pinnotheres* and pairs of commensal shrimp of the genus *Neopontonides*.

Another muddy-sand bottom dweller is the disk clam, *Dosinia discus* (Figure 3.33), a relative of the edible clam, *Mercenaria mercenaria*. *Dosinia* is laterally flattened and has a very smooth shell. It is an able burrower and its long, fused siphons permit it to bury itself several inches beneath the surface. It is the frequent prey of the moon snail, *Polinices duplicatus*, as evidenced by the many bored shells one finds on the beach.

Figure 3.29. The incongruous ark, *Anadara brasiliana*. (x 1)

Figure 3.30. The blood ark, *Anadara ovalis*. (x 1)

Figure 3.31. The ponderous ark, *Noetia ponderosa*. (x 1)

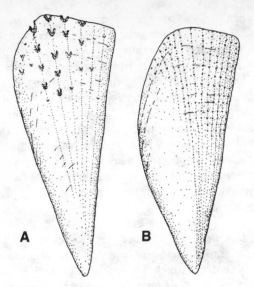

A   B

Figure 3.32. The pen shells, *Atrina serrata* (A) and *Atrina seminuda* (B). (x 0.5)

Figure 3.33. The disk clam, *Dosinia discus,* with a hole bored by *Polinices duplicatus.* (x 0.9)

Figure 3.34. The alternate tellin, *Tellina alternata.* (x 1)

The rose-petal tellin, *Tellina lineata,* and the alternate tellin, *Tellina alternata* (Figure 3.34), are two members of the family Tellinidae found along the Gulf Coast. Tellins, unlike the clams previously discussed, are not filter-feeders but deposit-feeders. They have very long, unfused siphons, enabling them to burrow

deeply. The incurrent siphon acts as a vacuum cleaner, sweeping over the sediment for edible detritus and algae. The shell of *Tellina alternata* may be flushed interiorly with pink or yellow. The shell of *Tellina lineata* is smaller, less elongate and flushed with pink. Of these two species, *Tellina alternata* is more common in beach wash along the northwestern Gulf Coast.

The Edible Blue Crab and Its Kin

Perhaps the best known crab along the Texas Coast is the edible blue crab, *Callinectes sapidus* (Figure 3.35). Another species of this genus, *Callinectes ornatus,* also occurs here. It may be distinguished by the six frontal teeth on its carapace margin in contrast to the four frontal teeth of *Callinectes sapidus* (Figure 3.36). In addition, *Callinectes ornatus* is smaller, reaching a width of 93 mm in contrast to the maximum width of 230 mm in *Callinectes sapidus.* Hence, it is of little commercial value; however, *Callinectes ornatus* is the most abundant crab in the shallow offshore areas. Berried females have been found at all times of the year, although they are most abundant during the winter months. It is eaten by several species of fish, including the tarpon and the ling.

Figure 3.35. The blue crab, *Callinectes sapidus.* (x 0.5)

A

B

Figure 3.36. Frontal carapace margins of *Callinectes ornatus* (A) and *Callinectes sapidus* (B).

Berried female *Callinectes sapidus* are found nearly year round, the peak of the breeding season being in June and July. During the breeding season one may often see a male carrying female beneath his body, waiting for her to molt. Mating can occur only when the female molts and her shell is soft enough to permit penetration of the male's penes through her genital pores. The transferred sperm are then used to fertilize the one to three million eggs produced by the female.

After mating the female migrates into deeper water where she attaches the fertilized eggs to her pleopods. The egg mass resembles a sponge, and the berried female is often called a "sponge" crab. The eggs hatch in about two weeks, releasing the young as zoeae (Figure 3.37). The zoea eventually molts into a megalops (Figure 3.38) which transforms into a diminutive adult form; few of these millions of zoea will escape predation and survive to adulthood. The crabs mature in one year, begin breeding and live perhaps two more years.

Figure 3.37. A crab zoea larva. (x 20)

Figure 3.38. A crab megalops larva. (x 10)

Callinectes is an omnivore; it eats fish, bottom invertebrates, vascular plants, and detritus. Old crabs, past their terminal molt, occasionally are found heavily encrusted with the barnacles *Balanus amphitrite niveus* and *Chelonibia patula*. *Chelonibia* (Figure 3.39) is a smooth-walled barnacle with a narrow operculum that seems too small for its aperture. When removed from the crab and turned upside down, numerous long septa extend from the wall into shell cavity of the barnacle. A larger relative, *Chelonibia testudinaria* (Figure 3.39), can be found on sea turtles.

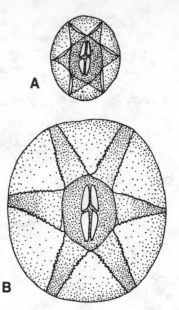

Figure 3.39. The acorn barnacles, *Chelonibia patula* (A) and *Chelonibia testudinaria* (B). (x 4)

The shells of barnacles on the bottom of the turtle are usually well worn from frequent contacts with the sandy bottom. Blue crabs also host the parasitic barnacle, *Octolasmis lowei* (Figure 3.40), in their gill chambers and may be infected with parasitic nemerteans and trematodes. *Octolasmis* resembles a miniature gooseneck barnacle with the calcareous valves reduced. It breeds in the summer, when its offspring develop through seven larval stages in the plankton before seeking a new host. This planktonic journey usually lasts about two weeks.

Figure 3.40. The parasitic barnacle, *Octolasmis lowei*. (x 10)

Figure 3.41. The speckled crab, *Arenaeus cribrarius*. (x 1)

Figure 3.42. Carapace and cheliped of *Portunus gibbesii* (x 0.5) (A) and *Portunus spinimanus* (x 0.5) (B).

Figure 3.43. The lady crab, *Ovalipes quadulpensis*. (x 0.8)

The speckled crab, *Arenaeus cribrarius* (Figure 3.41), is another representative of the swimming crab family found on this coast. *Arenaeus* is similar in shape to *Callinectes,* but is immediately distinguished by its sandy color and the pebbled pattern on its carapace. These crabs are common in the surf zone and subtidally range from Massachusetts to Brazil. *Arenaeus* usually buries itself in the sand. The heavy coat of hairlike setae on the sides of its mouthparts keeps sand away from delicate structures. When buried, the chelipeds are held close to the body. It respires by drawing water in around the lateral and posterior margins of the carapace and pumping it through the gill chamber and out the anterior end through the space between its body and chelipeds. Its gills are large for a crab of its size, providing additional oxygen for the exertion required by life among the breaking waves.

Several other swimming crabs, members of the genus *Portunus,* are found along this coast, none is especially common nearshore. The species that are usually found nearshore are *Portunus gibbesii* and *Portunus spinimanus* (Figure 3.42). The carapace of the latter species is less than twice as wide as it is long; the carapace of the former species is at least twice as wide as it is long. *Portunus* closely resembles *Callinectes,* but males may be easily distinguished: male *Portunus* have triangular abdomens; male *Callinectes* have "T-shaped" abdomens.

The lady crab, *Ovalipes guadulpensis* (Figure 3.43), also belongs to the family Portunidae. It is a very colorful crab, the carapace being yellow-gray to light lavender-gray with dull yellow spots. The spines on the carapace are purple. The last pair of walking legs,

Figure 3.44. The purse crab, *Persephona aguilonaris.* (x 1.3)

which are modified as paddles as in all portunid crabs, are lemon yellow. It lives primarily on sandy bottoms and is occasionally found swimming near the jetties.

The purse crab, *Persephona aguilonaris* (Figure 3.44), is slow moving and cryptic in its behavior. It buries itself in the sand by vertical movement of its legs until only its eyes and the front portion of its carapace remain exposed. Its common name derives

from the size and shape of the female's abdomen which extends over the entire undersurface of the crab. When *Persephona* is gravid, this abdomen covers the eggs attached to the pleopods. It is easily recognized by its circular carapace, which is cream colored with red blotches.

Spider Crabs

Two species of spider crabs occur along our coast, *Libinia emarginata* and *Libinia dubia* (Figure 3.45), which can be distinguished by the number of spines in the median row on the carapace. *Libinia emarginata* has more than 7 spines (usually 9) in this row, and *Libinia dubia* has 7 or fewer spines (usually 6). Both species are slow moving and cryptic. Sexual maturity follows the terminal molt; thus the females mate with hardened carapace.

Young *Libinia* are commensal with the cabbagehead medusa, *Stomolophus meleagris*. They are often found riding in the bell of this large jellyfish. Adult *Libinia* can be found on pilings or in grass flats, where their unusual shape helps to camouflage them. They are most common during the summer months, which is their peak breeding season.

Figure 3.45. The spider crab, *Libinia dubia.* (x 1)

Flotsam and Jetsam

The waves that wash up on the beach often carry organisms whose normal habitat is in deeper water on the continental shelf or adrift far at sea. Storm waves deposit the shells of numerous mollusks, including the heavy shells of the snail *Murex fulvescens,* on the beach. Unfavorable winds often carry the Portuguese man-of-war, *Physalia physalis;* the by-the-wind sailor, *Velella velella;* and the purple storm snails, *Janthina* spp., onto the beach. Most of these organisms are dead and badly battered by the time the beachcomber finds them, presenting a confusing array of broken shells and jellied blobs to the inexperienced collector. A little experience with intact specimens enables the average collector to identify most of these fragments.

Several species inhabit driftwood and other objects floating at sea. Among the more conspicuous of these are the stalked barnacles, *Lepas anatifera, Lepas anserifera* and *Lepas pectinata,* which are commonly found on styrofoam floats and bottles as well as driftwood. Like other barnacles they are permanently attached to their substrate and obtain their food by filtering plankton from the water with their long, curved feet. *Lepas anatifera* (Figure 4.1) has a shell marked by very fine lines; the other two species have deeply grooved shells. *Lepas anserifera* has five or six

pairs of filtering appendages, whereas the scaled goose barnacle, *Lepas pectinata,* has fewer than three pairs of filtering appendages.

Breaking open pieces of driftwood may expose the boring clams *Bankia gouldi* (Figure 4.2) or *Teredo bartschi,* or the boring isopod (or gribble), *Limnoria tripunctata.* The burrows taper toward the outside of the block of wood (as the clam bores into the wood, it grows and makes a wider burrow), and are the only evidence of boring clams usually found in the driftwood (Figure 4.3). The burrows of *Bankia* have a calcareous lining. The shells of *Bankia* and *Teredo* are greatly reduced and thus these clams appear more like worms. *Limnoria* (Figure 4.4) is a small isopod about 5 millimeters long. It bores holes about 13 millimeters deep in wooden structures such as pilings. *Bankia* tunnels most rapidly in hard, dry wood, and usually avoids soft, rotten wood.

Figure 4.2. The wood-boring clam, *Bankia gouldi.* (x 2)

Figure 4.3. Driftwood bored by *Bankia gouldi.* (x 0.5)

Figure 4.1. Two gooseneck barnacles, *Lepas anatifera,* attached to a piece of driftwood. (x 1)

Figure 4.4. The wood-boring isopod, *Limnoria tripunctata*. (x 5)

Once a piece of driftwood has settled on the beach and partially dried out, it may be inhabited by a variety of terrestrial creatures such as insects, scorpions and pseudoscorpions. Most of the marine species will be dead by this time, and their burrows provide ready-made places for the terrestrial invaders.

Portuguese Man-of-War

One of the most conspicuous objects on the beach is the pale purple float of the Portuguese man-of-war, *Physalia physalis* (Figure 4.5). Having the appearance of a partially inflated balloon, this "toy" is really a booby trap. Beneath the float and often stretched across the beach for several meters are dozens of nearly invisible tentacles armed with nematocysts. These nematocysts may be active long after the rest of the animal seems quite dead. Like bee stings and spider bites, contact with nematocysts produces different reactions in different people and may be fatal. *Physalia* is actually a colony of smaller animals called zooids, and each is highly specialized for bearing the nematocysts, digesting food or forming the float. The float is filled with a mixture of gases, similar to air and secreted by an oval disc at the base of the float. The Portuguese man-of-war usually floats in schools at the mercy of ocean currents and winds which occasionally drive them onto the shore. When driven into the bays *Physalia* feeds primarily on anchovies and other small fish.

The upper portion of *Physalia's* float is compressed into a small "sail" mounted diagonally on the float. Two forms have been found: a left-sailing form, with the sail extending from the upper left corner to the lower right corner when viewing the *Physalia* along its long axis; and a right-sailing form, with the sail extending from the upper right corner to the lower left corner. The left-sailing form predominates in the Gulf of Mexico.

Purple Sailors and Bubble Rafts

Two close relatives of *Physalia*, the by-the-wind sailor, *Velella velella* (Figure 4.6) and its cousin *Porpita porpita* (Figure 4.7), may also be beached by onshore winds. *Velella's* float is modified to form a sail, from which it gets its name, and a horizontal base across which the sail is mounted diagonally. Like *Physalia*, two forms exist with the left-sailing form being the most common in the Gulf of Mexico. *Porpita's* float is a round disk resembling the cross section of a

Figure 4.6. The by-the-wind sailor, *Velella velella*. (x 1)

Figure 4.7. *Porpita porpita*. (x 1)

Figure 4.5. The Portuguese man-of-war, *Physalia physalis*. (x 1)

tree trunk. It lacks a sail. Unlike that of *Physalia*, the floats of *Velella* and *Porpita* are chitinous and thus remain adrift long after the animal has died. These floats are valuable as substrates upon which some surface-dwelling animals lay their eggs and to which barnacles and hydroids attach. The floats are often all that is found of these species on the beach. The softer parts of the animals decay rapidly. The tissues of *Velella* and *Porpita* are usually bluish and their floats are usually translucent white. *Porpita* is limited more to tropical waters than *Velella* and *Physalia* and hence is less often found in the northern Gulf.

Although an occasional Portuguese man-of-war falls prey to a sea turtle or a gooseneck barnacle, perhaps the most significant predators of *Physalia* and its kin are the purple storm snails *Janthina* spp. Three species of *Janthina* are common to the northwestern Gulf of Mexico: *Janthina janthina*, *Janthina pallida* and *Janthina prolongata* (Figure 4.8). These species can be distinguished by the shape of the shell. *Janthina janthina* is the largest species found locally, reaching a diameter of over 4 centimeters, and its shell is squatter and more angular than the other species. The shells of *Janthina prolongata* and *Janthina pallida* are smaller and more rounded, the lip of the former being slightly more slender and pointed than the latter. *Janthina* constructs a bubble raft by coating trapped bubbles of air with mucous. The raft and *Janthina's* very thin shell enable it to stay afloat. Since the snail must be at the sea surface to trap air, a snail separated from its raft beneath the surface is doomed to sink and starve or be eaten.

When it comes in contact with a *Physalia* or *Velella*, *Janthina* extends its proboscis to its prey and rasps away at its tissues. A pair of *Janthina* can consume a 10 centimeter long *Physalia* is less than one day. If its usual prey is scarce, *Janthina* may resort to can-nibalism. These snails, particularly *Janthina janthina*, are countershaded. They are pale blue on top and deep purple underneath. However, they float upside down, so that the pale side faces down. From below looking up the pale side blends in with the sky, and above them looking down the dark side blends in with the deep sea.

A blue nudibranch, *Glaucus atlanticus* (Figure 4.9), also feeds on *Physalia* and its kin. *Glaucus* floats upside down at the sea surface with the aid of six frilled lobes containing gas-filled pockets. It may also catch a ride on its floating prey.

Figure 4.9. The pelagic nudibranch, *Glaucus atlanticus*. (x 3)

Figure 4.10. The onion anemone, *Paranthus rapiformis*, inflated (left) and buried in the sand (right). (x 1)

Onions from the Sea

Occasionally the onion anemone, *Paranthus rapiformis* (Figure 4.10), will wash up on the beach. This anemone is so named because, when disturbed it pulls in its tentacles and inflates itself with water. Its translucent white color with longitudinal white stripes gives it the appearance of a boiling onion. It usually lives in deeper water offshore, but will bury itself up to its tentacles in the sand and look right at home if washed into shallow water.

Figure 4.8. The purple storm snails, *Janthina prolongata* (A), *Janthina janthina* (B) and *Janthina unbilicata* (C). (x 1.5)

Figure 4.11. The Sargassum community: the sargassumfish, *Histrio histrio;* the nudibranch, *Scyllaea pelagica;* the sargassum crab, *Portunus sayi;* the sargassum shrimp, *Latreutes fucorum;* and the polychaete worm, *Platynereis dumerilii.* (x 0.8)

The Floating *Sargassum* Community

The Gulf Coast lacks the giant seaweeds or kelp that are common along the Pacific and North Atlantic coasts. Consequently, beach litter consisting of up-rooted or broken fragments of seaweed are relatively scarce. One notable exception is the pelagic seaweed *Sargassum* spp. (Figure 4.11). *Sargassum* is buoyed by small air bladders and is transported by the same currents that bring *Physalia* and *Velella.* Hence, it washes up on our beaches sporadically and brings with it a fascinating community of specialized creatures. Many of these animals have shapes and colors that blend in with the sargassum. Some of these animals, such as the hydroids and the sargassum anemone, *Anemonia sargassensis,* are sessile; others, such as the flatworms, polychaetes, shrimps and crabs, crawl about on the surface of the drifting seaweed. Still others, such as the sargassumfish, *Histrio histrio,* and the young of certain other oceanic fish, are free-swimming and use the sargassum as a refuge from larger, predacious fish.

Although *Histrio* can swim quite rapidly, it often crawls through the seaweed, using its pectoral fins like arms. *Histrio* is a member of the frogfish family but is much more ornate than its relatives. Its irregular out-line and mottled coloration help it to blend in with its leafy environment. Similarly, the carnivorous nudibranch, *Scyllaea pelagica* (Figure 4.12), has large leaflike lobes along its back and an orange-brown and yellow coloration that make it almost impossible to distinguish from its plant host. The sargassum crabs *Portunus sayi* (Figure 4.13) and *Callinectes marginatus* and the shrimp *Latreutes fucorum* also sport a mottled brown disguise. The small sargassum flatworm *Gnesioceros sargassicola* (Figure 4.14) is a tawny gray color flecked with reddish-brown spots.

Figure 4.12. The nudibranch, *Scyllaea pelagica.* (x 0.7)

Figure 4.13. The sargassum crab, *Portunus sayi*. (x 2)

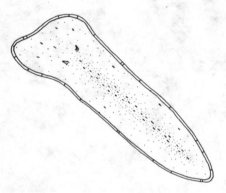

Figure 4.14. The flatworm, *Gnesioceros sargassicola*. (x 4)

Figure 4.15. The ostrich-plume hydroid, *Algaophenia late-carinata,* attached to a Sargassum float. (x 2.5)

The delicate appearance of the sargassum is enhanced by the numerous fernlike hydroids and intricate bryozoans that grow over its surface. Some hydroid species have a high degree of fidelity to certain varieties of sargassum and have been used as a means of classifying sargassum assemblages. Hence the hydroid fauna found on sargassum varies greatly, depending upon the variety of sargassum collected. *Gonothyraea gracilis* and the ostrich plume hydroid,

Aglaophenia late-carinata (Figure 4.15), are among the more common hydroids on sargassum washed ashore along the northwestern Gulf Coast. The polychaete worms *Platynereis dumerilii* and *Harmothoë aculeata* are also common on the sargassum on these beaches. *Platynereis* is a pale yellow worm with a bright red stripe running the length of its back. This stripe is actually a blood vessel and the pulses of blood can be easily observed under a low power microscope. *Harmothoë* is a scaleworm which is easily recognized by the 15 pairs of large, fringed plates or scales extending over its back.

The sargassum fauna is closely related to and is undoubtedly derived from the littoral fauna. However, it is a dwarf fauna, the species found on sargassum being generally smaller than their relatives living on the shore. It is also a warm-water fauna which is best developed in areas where the water temperature exceeds 18°C. Most of these animals abandon the sargassum when it is washed in or die and are washed out of the seaweed in the surf. A few of the more tenacious species can be dislodged by vigorously shaking freshly beached sargassum. A much better impression of this interesting fauna is gained by collecting fresh sargassum from the sea with a dip net or bucket and examining it in detail.

The sea spider, *Endeis spinosa* (Figure 4.16), is often observed crawling over sargassum clumps placed in a bucket of water. Not truly a spider, *Endeis* does not produce silk nor poison, but is equipped with a long proboscis with which it attacks bryozoans and hydroids found on the sargassum. Its long legs are adapted to clinging to its plant host; thus it is much more sluggish than true spiders. Male *Endeis* have an extra pair of small legs, known as ovigerous legs, with which they carry egg clusters until the eggs hatch.

Figure 4.16. The sea spider, *Endeis spinosa*. (x 12)

5

Offshore Bottoms: The Shrimp Grounds

Much of the continental shelf of the northern Gulf of Mexico, from just beyond the waves breaking on the beaches to a depth of about 200 meters, is intensively combed by shrimp trawlers in search of living gold. Large populations of commercial shrimp migrate vertically during the day, between the bays and the Gulf as they mature, and along the coast in search of food or some other requirement—perpetually keeping the fishermen guessing. So motile and elusive are these shrimp that as a boat crosses the bottom with two 75-foot wide nets deployed, a second boat following the same path 15 minutes later can catch nearly as many shrimp as the first boat. Trawling at three knots, a shrimp boat may cover over 500 acres (over 200 hectares) of bottom in an eight hour tow.

Otter trawls catch many animals other than shrimp. Fish, crabs, lobster, snails, clams, squid, and sea stars are among the "cull" that must be isolated from the marketable shrimp catch. Numerous other cohabitants are too small to be retained by the coarse-meshed nets. Among these are polychaete worms, the numerically dominant macroscopic animals throughout most of this habitat and a major food resource of commercial shrimp. Polychaetes also make up a large portion of the diets of demersal fishes, such as porgies, batfish, flounders, and tonguefish.

Animal populations inhabiting this seemingly homogeneous seascape respond differently to subtle changes in the characteristics of this environment. Shrimp, crabs, and other animals living on the sediment surface are sensitive to differences in temperature, salinity, and water depth. Various worms, clams, and other animals that burrow are also sensitive to sediment texture. Shell fragments and sand grains are materials used in the construction of burrows. Particle sizes in the adjacent sediment affect the ease of burrowing and the durability of burrows. Grain size also reflects local current patterns which distribute the sediments and transport suspended food along the bottom.

Animals that construct permanent burrows generally prefer coarser sediments than species that move continuously. The motile species are also able to survive in offshore areas where food is not abundant and must be sought out, whereas sedentary species are generally plentiful in nearshore areas where high productivity and steady currents assure a supply of food for those who sit and wait. Most of the food consumed by offshore benthic animals is imported, either as organic matter carried to the Gulf by rivers or as plankton production near the sea surface. This food is mixed with less nutritious sediment particles as it rains on the sea floor. One common means of obtaining this food is by deposit feeding, i.e. by simply swallowing sediment and extracting the nourishing components chemically in the gut. Undigested sediment is extruded as feces into small mounds. These mounds are a common sight on the bottom. Deposit feeding may occur either directly by swallowing sediment while burrowing through it or indirectly by intercepting sediment with outstretched tentacles or proboscis as it falls from the surface. Filter-feeding, which usually involves extension of the tentacles vertically to intercept food drifting with currents across the bottom, is common among sedentary species. Occasional arrivals of larger bits of detritus and deaths of indigenous animals support the scavengers. Predators consume living residents.

Each of these feeding modes is represented among the polychaetes, the most abundant macroscopic animals living in soft bottoms in the Gulf. Polychaete dominance is challenged locally by brief blooms of amphipods, anemone or surf clam populations, but the ecological importance of this diverse taxon is seldom diminished. Eighty-seven of the 100 most abundant macroinfaunal species in the eastern Gulf of Mexico are polychaetes.

The Ubiquitous Fauna

The sedentary polychaetes *Diopatra cuprea*, *Paraprionospio pinnata*, and *Clymenella torquata*, and the errant polychaete *Glycera americana*, are among the most ubiquitous offshore species in the Gulf. *Diopatra* (Figure 3.12) is also one of our most colorful species. Its irridescent reddish-brown body is often speckled with gray dots and is lined with yellow-brown parapodia speckled with green as a background for its bright red gills. Its durable tubes of shell fragments woven into a parchment-like lining project like crude periscopes from the sea floor. Once abandoned, these tubes are eventually extracted from the ever-shifting seascape and washed onto Gulf beaches. The tube seems to function as a food-gathering device as well as a residence for its omnivorous inhabitant. *Diopatra* consumes algae, copepods, gastropods, cumaceans, and barnacle larvae, many of which are commonly found on the outer surface of the tube.

The bamboo worm, *Clymenella torquata* (Figure 5.1), inhabits a straight vertical sand tube. Its 22 segments are long and slender, superficially resembling a bamboo stalk. *Clymenella* resides head down in its tube and uses the funnel-like anal segment characteristic of its family to plug the surficial end of the tube. This position enables it to ingest sediment from the bottom of its tube and deposit its wastes at the sediment surface, where they are readily swept away by currents or surge. Bamboo worms draw sufficient water into the tube from the top to irrigate the tube every 15-20 minutes, which enables them to survive in

anoxic sediments. Unlike many other tube-dwelling worms, *Clymenella* enjoys such a tight fit in its tube that it is unable to turn around. Because it must expose its tail to watchful predators during excretion, it has adopted unusual hastiness in this activity. However, should it miscalculate, it can regenerate the lost segments. *Clymenella torquata* is usually orange or green. The lesser bamboo worm, *Clymenella zonalis,* is always orange.

The bloodworm, *Glycera americana* (Figure 5.2), preys on other benthic invertebrates, particularly other polychaetes and amphipods. Juveniles typically construct burrows consisting of a network of waiting tubes from which they ambush passing prey. Adults are more motile but usually remain buried to avoid detection by shrimp or fish. Bloodworms detect their prey by sensing the pressure wave passing in front of a moving visitor. *Glycera's* proboscis is rapidly everted to expose its four large jaws, which seize the hapless victim. Bloodworms swarm at the sea surface during their breeding season and die shortly after releasing their gametes. *Paraprionospio pinnata* (Figure 5.3) is a selective deposit feeding worm related to the blister worm found in oyster shells.

Another ubiquitous worm-like species is the nemertean, *Cerebratulus lacteus* (Figure 7.13). Like *Glycera, Cerebratulus* captures its prey by everting its proboscis with surprising speed to snare unsuspecting passersby. The sharp-knobbed nassa, *Nassarius*

Figure 5.2. Anterior end of the bloodworm, *Glycera americana*, with extended proboscis exposing its four teeth. (x 3)

Figure 5.1. The bamboo worm, *Clymenella torquata;* (A) posterior end, (B) anterior end, and (C) entire worm in its tube. (x 5)

Figure 5.3. Anterior end of *Paraprionospio pinnata*. (x 5)

Figure 5.4. Shell of the sharp-knobbed nassa, *Nassarius acutus*. (x 8)

Figure 5.5. The peanut worm, *Phascolion strombi*, inhabiting a shell of *Epitonium*. (x 8)

Figure 5.6. Shell of the Atlantic abra, *Abra aequalis*. (x 1.3)

Figure 5.7. The phoronid, *Phoronid architecta*. (x 1.8)

acutus, the Atlantic abra, *Abra aequalis,* and the phoronid, *Phoronis architecta,* are also widely distributed in the northern Gulf.

Fish or crab corpses rapidly attract numerous minute scavengers. *Nassarius acutus* (Figure 5.4) has a keen sense of smell which enables it to quickly locate decaying flesh. This response is easily observed by allowing several of these snails to burrow into the sand layer at the bottom of a small bowl filled with clean seawater and slowly adding a few drops of the liquor from clam, crab, or fish flesh homogenized in a blender. The detection range of these scavengers can be observed by replacing the bowl with a long trough and adding the liquor at one end. Hungry snails work best.

Usually quiescent and buried with only its proboscis probing through the sediment surface to test the passing water, this snail pops to the sand surface in startling abundance when the sediment is disturbed. Waving its proboscis, *Nassarius* seems to engage in a frantic search for some uncovered morsel lest the sea reclaim it as rapidly as it appeared. *Nassarius acutus* is apparently more resistant or resilient than most benthic invertebrates to the summer anoxia which develops off the Louisiana coast, and its abundance enables it to play a major role in disposing of the carcasses of less fortunate organisms.

Nassarius acutus is more slender than its congener in the bays, *Nassarius vibex* (Figure 7.16), and as its name suggests, the knobs on its white or yellowish shell are more pronounced. When rotting flesh is not readily available, *Nassarius* will attack live prey or eggs it finds on the bottom.

Small shells of deceased snails such as *Nassarius* are often utilized by the tiny hermit crab *Pagurus bonairensis* or the peanut worm, *Phascolion strombi* (Figure 5.5). More sedentary than the hermit crab, *Phascolion* wedges its bulbous trunk into the shell and

cements sand grains or shell fragments over the aperture, leaving only a small hole through which it can extend its long neck-like introvert and crown of feeding tentacles. As its name suggests, the introvert can be withdrawn into the trunk if disturbed, as may occur when a nearby hermit crab begins searching for a new shell. *Abra aequalis* (Figure 5.6) is also quite small (about 6 millimeters). This deposit-feeding clam has a very smooth shell, which is usually white but often with a yellowish cast.

The phoronid, *Phoronis architecta* (Figure 5.7), is a small, worm-like animal that dwells in a vertical chitinous tube in the sea floor. Like the brachiopods and bryozoans, it has a spiralled crown of feeding tentacles called a lophophore. *Phoronis* is only about 1-1.5 centimeters long and its narrow tube is about four times its length. The tube is flexible and usually covered with a single layer of sand grains. Its lower end is rounded and closed. *Phoronis* has a U-shaped gut, bringing its anus back up to the single opening in the tube. The anterior two-thirds of *Phoronis* is flesh colored, and the posterior end is a dark yellowish red, resulting from a concentration of haemoglobin in this end. Unlike most other phoronids, *Phoronis architecta* has separate sexes.

The brachiopod, *Glottidia pyramidata* (Figure 5.8), also lives in a vertical burrow and filters suspended food with a lophophore. However, *Glottidia's* burrow is lined with mucous-impregnated sand, and except for its long pedicle, its body is encased in a bivalved shell composed of calcium phosphate. These shells rarely wash out of the burrows after the death of the brachiopods; they decay in the burrows and thus are seldom found by shell collectors. *Glottidia* typically remains in its burrow, which is easily identified by its slit-like opening, but it can rebury itself if displaced. The likelihood of such displacement may be reduced by attaching the end of its pedicle to a buried shell. If completely covered by shifting sand, *Glottidia* can also dig itself out.

Glottidia spawns about 10,000 eggs during a full, or occasionally a new, moon, when tidal flushing is great enough to carry them seaward. Its larvae spend about three weeks in the plankton before settling as they are carried shoreward by tidal currents. Willits and moon snails are its major predators. The exposed edge of its shell is often exploited as an attachment site by hydroids and algae and by snails as deposition sites for their egg capsules.

Figure 5.8. The brachiopod, *Glottidia pyramidata,* in its burrow. (x 1)

Figure 5.9. Anterior end of the roofing worm, *Owenia fusiformis,* encased in its sand tube. (x 10)

Nearshore Worms and Neighbors

Less widespread species are often characteristic of special environments to which they are particularly sensitive. Sensitivities to temperature and salinity generally constrain the distribution of marine species. As these parameters are similar over large areas of ocean bottom, subtler variables often assume greater importance. Epifaunal species, i.e. species living on the surface of the sea floor, frequently respond to differences in water depth or distance from shore. Infaunal species, i.e. those burrowing into the sediments, are usually sensitive to sediment type. Organisms living nearshore must be more tolerant of variable temperature and salinity and high turbidity than those living offshore. However, food is frequently more abundant nearshore, and for several epifaunal species, proximity to nursery areas within the bays is an important asset of the nearshore environment.

In the fine sand that characterizes most of the nearshore sediments in the northwestern Gulf, the infauna is dominated by polychaetes such as *Magelona phyllisae, Mediomastus californiensis, Scoloplos rubra, Phyllodoce mucosa, Stenelais boa, Aglaophamus verrilli, Owenia fusiformis, Neanthes succinea, Lumbrineris tenuis,* and *Spiophanes bombyx.* The roofing worm, *Owenia fusiformis* (Figure 5.9), prefers to construct its long, flexible tube in areas of fairly clean sand. It selects flat, light colored sand grains and arranges them like overlapping roof tiles with the free edges facing upward. In mature worms this tube may be 15-20 centimeters long and 2-5 millimeters wide. *Owenia* is a versatile ciliary mucous feeder. Its feeding crown is drawn out into eight branching lobes that intercept and channel suspended food to its mouth, but it may also bend over to pick up larger food particles from the bottom near its tube. This crown may be light red, brown, or greenish in color and is infused with in elaborate network of blood vessels, which enables it to function as a respiratory as well as feeding structure.

Like *Capitella capitata* (Figure 5.10), *Mediomastus californiensis* (Figure 5.11) has poorly developed parapodia and prostomium and thus may be mistaken for an oligochaete. Its head region, or prostomium, lacks eyes, tentacles, and palps. Its well developed setae are typically much longer on the anterior eleven segments, the thorax, than on the rest of the body. Unlike *Mediomastus, Capitella* has only 9 thoracic segments and possesses genital spines on the eighth and ninth segments. *Mediomastus* is a very small, slender worm, about 1-2 cm long, which is commonly found in estuarine marshes as well as offshore.

Scoloplos capensis and *Scoloplos rubra* (Figure 5.12) also lack appendages or eyes on their heads. However, their heads are pointed and their parapodia are developed as gills. These gills, or branchiae, begin at about the fifth or sixth segment in *Scoloplos rubra*, but not until segment 13 or 14 in *Scoloplos capensis*. The thoracic region of these worms is somewhat flattened with dense clusters of short setae along the sides. The posterior portion of the worm is cylindrical with

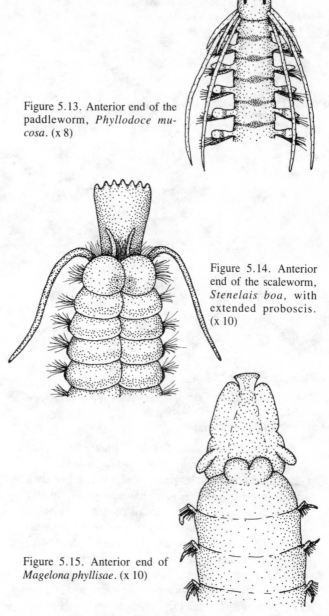

Figure 5.13. Anterior end of the paddleworm, *Phyllodoce mucosa*. (x 8)

Figure 5.14. Anterior end of the scaleworm, *Stenelais boa*, with extended proboscis. (x 10)

Figure 5.15. Anterior end of *Magelona phyllisae*. (x 10)

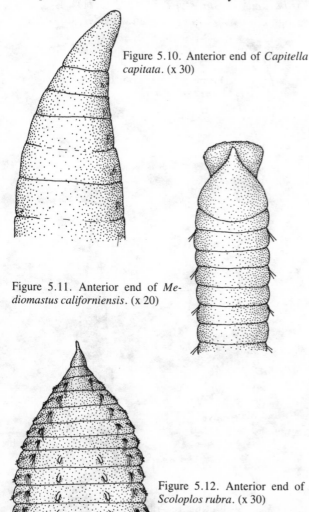

Figure 5.10. Anterior end of *Capitella capitata*. (x 30)

Figure 5.11. Anterior end of *Mediomastus californiensis*. (x 20)

Figure 5.12. Anterior end of *Scoloplos rubra*. (x 30)

fewer setae. *Scoloplos capensis* usually has brown bars across its thorax beginning at the ninth segment, whereas *Scoloplos rubra* is reddish in color, as its name suggests. The paddleworm, *Phyllodoce mucosa* (Figure 5.13), uses its large paddle-like parapodia to move rapidly through the sand. The scaleworm, *Stenlais boa* (Figure 5.14), is protected by a double row of overlapping plates along its back and captures its prey with a knobby eversible proboscis.

Magelona phyllisae (Figure 5.15) is also a nonselective deposit feeder. It is easily distinguished from other genera of worms by its flattened, spade-like prostomium, which may spread beyond the width of its long, slender trunk. *Magelona* burrows through the sediment in search of food and does not construct sub-

Figure 5.16. Anterior end of *Spiophanes bombyx*. (x 15)

Figure 5.17. Anterior end of *Aglaophamus verrilli*. (x 20)

Figure 5.18. Anterior end of *Lumbrineris tenuis*. (x 10)

equipped with stiff setae, which anchor the worm within the tube, and a pair of larger cutting setae, which are used to remove partitions or slice open the tube when it must be enlarged to accommodate a growing worm.

These polychaetes share sandy habitats with other burrowing animals, such as the onion anemone, *Paranthus rapiformis* (Figure 4.10), the dwarf tellin, *Tellina versicolor,* and the fine-ribbed auger, *Terebra protexta* (Figure 5.20). The dwarf tellin is common on sandy bottoms. Its translucent shell is often marked with pink rays and is less than 2 centimeters long. This deposit feeder is restricted to the surficial sediments by its short siphons. The shell of *Tellina versicolor* is more rectangular than those of other common tellins.

Spring Bloomers

During spring this sandy bottom fauna is joined by the surf clam, *Mulinia lateralis* (Figure 7.5), the hermit crab, *Pagurus bonairensis,* the amphipod, *Corophium ascherusicum,* the cumacean, *Oxyurostylis salinoi,* and the lancelet, *Branchiostoma caribaeum. Oxyurostylis* (Figure 5.21), is easily recognized by its ovate body and slender, forked tail.

Figure 5.19. Anterior end of *Spiochaetopterus costarum*. (x 2)

stantial tubes. *Spiophanes bombyx* (Figure 5.16) constructs more durable tubes, from which it selectively ingests food particles. Its prostomium is marked by a pair of anterior horns. *Aglaophamus verrilli* (Figure 5.17) is an omnivore whose small prostomium belies the threat of its eversible pharynx. *Lumbrineris tenuis* (Figure 5.18) is a predator. Its simple dome-like prostomium lacks eyes, palps, or tentacles.

Unlike its relative in the sand flats (Figure 7.20), the parchment worm, *Spiochaetopterus costarum* (Figure 5.19), lives in a straight tube oriented vertically in the sediment. Rather than the constricted ends characteristic of *Chaetopterus* tubes, *Spiochaetopterus* tubes have perforated partitions across the buried end of the tube. These partitions help prevent tube collapse and maintain water pressure in the tube while permitting water to flow into the pore spaces between sand grains beneath the tube. This flow of water is maintained by cilia on modified parapodia in the middle body region. As this water passes the anterior portion of the body, suspended food is entrapped in mucous bags secreted by specialized parapodia. The long palps are equipped with ciliated gutters which probably functioned as a means of food capture in the ancestors of this worm, but presently help to eject fecal pellets and other debris from the tube. The anteriormost segments are

Figure 5.20. Shell of the fine-ribbed auger, *Terebra protexta*. (x 1.8)

Figure 5.21. The cumacean, *Oxyurostylis salinoi*. (x 15)

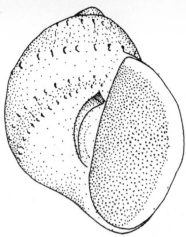

Figure 5.23. Shell of the Atlantic natica, *Natica canrena*. (x 8)

It spends most of its time buried in the sand with only the tip of its head exposed. Burial is accomplished by excavating a hole with its hind legs and backing into it. A respiratory and feeding current is set up by movement of the epipodites of the anterior legs, forcing surface water over the gills and filtering mouthparts. The antennae are much longer in the active male than in the more sedentary female, and usually are carried back over the carapace.

Patches of coarse, shelly sand are often inhabited by the lancelet, *Branchiostoma caribaeum* (Figure 5.22). Resembling a small fish, this primitive chordate lives partially buried in the sediment, where it filters suspended food borne by passing currents. It seems to prefer areas where there is moderate water movement from subsurface waves or tidal currents. Its feeding mechanism is similar to that of the sea squirt. Food-laden water is drawn into the pharynx and passes through two rows of narrow slits which retain the food but allow the water to escape to the sea. The mouth is protected by a circlet of tentacles which help to exclude unwanted debris and sand. Adults are about 5 centimeters long.

culum is calcareous with a white exposed surface, in contrast to the thin amber operculum of *Polinices*. *Tectonatica* is less than 1 centimeter long, but is easily distinguished from juveniles of the two larger species by its closed umbilicus. The miniature natica is fairly common near shore, but its small size hides it from the casual observer. Each of these snails preys on clams and other snails.

The fragile paranoid worm, *Aricidea fragilis* (Figure 5.24), prefers silty sand to coarser sediments. Its head has a single median antenna and its back is obscured by numerous pairs of antenna-like gills. *Aricidea* is a nonselective deposit feeder that is found in very shallow water as well as offshore.

The reddish echiuroid worm, *Thalassema hartmani* (Figure 5.25), is often found near passes and in

Figure 5.24. Anterior end of *Aricidea fragilis*. (x 20)

Figure 5.22. The lancelet, *Branchiostoma caribaeum*. (x 3)

Several moon snails occur on the shrimp grounds. The familiar nearshore moon snail, *Polinices duplicatus* (Figure 3.9), is also found to moderate depths, where it is joined by the colorful Atlantic natica, *Natica canrena* (Figure 5.23), and the miniature natica, *Tectonatica pusilla*. Unlike the shell of *Polinices*, *Natica's* shell is usually marked by sprial stripes accented by dark brown bands, *Natica's* oper-

Figure 5.25. The echiuroid worm, *Thalassema hartmani*. (x 7)

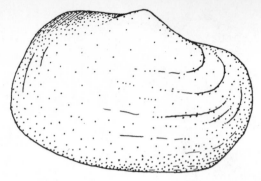

Figure 5.26. The commensal clam, *Paramya subovata*. (x 9)

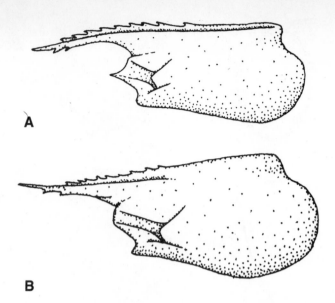

Figure. 5.28. Carapaces of commercial shrimp; (A) *Penaeus aztecus* or *Penaeus duorarum*, (B) *Penaues setiferus*. (x 1)

dredged areas. *Thalassema* is a deposit feeder that lives with its proboscis extended over the sea floor to ensnare drifting particles of food. A small, fragile clam, *Paramya subovata* (Figure 5.26), and a pinnotherid crab, *Pinnixa lunzi*, are frequently caught with *Thalassema*, and may be commensal with it, as is characteristic of several cohabitants of echiuroid worm burrows in California.

Shrimp for the Table and Aquarium

Of the many species of shrimp that inhabit the shallow waters of the Gulf of Mexico, three species are sufficiently large and abundant to be fished profitably. These shrimp, members of the family Penaeidae, are the brown shrimp, *Penaeus aztecus*, the pink shrimp, *Penaeus duorarum*, and the white shrimp, *Penaeus setiferus* (Figure 5.27). These species differ from most similar shrimps in that the ventral surface of the rostrum is lined with teeth. They also have a deep groove along either side of the rostrum, which extends nearly to the posterior end of the carapace in brown shrimp and pink shrimp, but terminates near the base of the rostrum in white shrimp (Figure 5.28). Adult pink shrimp typically have a dark spot on each side of the abdomen, overlapping the third and fourth segments.

These shrimp are most active at night, often swimming to the surface in shallow water, where they can

Figure 5.27. The white shrimp, *Penaeus setiferus*. (x 0.3)

be caught in the surface-skimming butterfly nets used by many fishermen in Louisiana. During the day the pink shrimp and brown shrimp often burrow into the substrate. White shrimp seldom burrow and are usually caught while they are resting on the bottom during the daylight hours. Man is not the only shrimp predator. Such fishes as sand perch and sea robins also enjoy this delicacy.

A commercial shrimp spends part of its life offshore and part in bays connected to the Gulf by passes. Mating and spawning take place offshore. *Penaeus aztecus* breed year round at depths of 50 to 120 meters; individuals in shallower water do not breed in the coldest months, i.e. January and February. *Penaeus setiferus* inhabits shallower water (14 to 50 meters) and spawns mostly in the fall.

When these shrimp mate, a spermatophore, i.e. a capsule containing sperm borne on the modified second pair of pleopods of the male, is transferred to the female's gonopores. These gonopores are found on the bases of her third pair of walking legs. When conditions are suitable, the female releases her one-half to one million eggs and they are fertilized as they pass through her gonopores. Twenty-four hours later the drifting eggs hatch as nauplii and begin a planktonic existence. After five molts the egg yolk is exhausted, and the nauplius transforms into a protozoea, then a mysis, and finally a postlarva, which enters the bays to become a bottom dweller. It remains in the bays and estuaries until it is nearly mature. It then migrates offshore, matures and breeds, thus completing its life cycle.

The sugar shrimp, *Parapenaeus longirostris* (Figure 5.29), can be readily distinguished from the commercial shrimps of the genus *Penaeus* in that it lacks teeth on the ventral edge of its rostrum. These teeth are replaced by a pronounced comb of setae. Its eyes are green and its tail is often tipped with red. It is not sought commercially in the Gulf of Mexico, but is moderately abundant and undoubtedly mixed with catches of other species, and thus is sold commercially. Individuals of this species in the Mediterranean Sea reach a much larger size than those in the Gulf and are exploited off the Tunisian coast.

Three other species of shrimp supplement commercial catches in some portions of their ranges. The seabob, *Xiphopeneus krøyeri* (Figure 5.30), is commercially important in South America and can be immediately recognized by its long, upcurved rostrum. It is found near shore, although it does not enter the bays because it is apparently unable to tolerate low salinities. Two smaller shrimp, *Trachypeneus constrictus* (Figure 5.31) and *Trachypeneus similus*, are harvested off southern Florida. Like *Parapenaeus*, *Trachypeneus* lacks teeth on the lower surface of its rostrum, but also lacks the fixed spines near the end of the telson characteristic of the former genus. The last three segments of *Trachypeneus'* abdomen have a sharp keel, or carina. In *Trachypeneus similis* these segments are covered by a pubescence, which is limited to the region of the carina in *Trachypeneus constrictus*.

The rock shrimp, *Sicyonia dorsalis* (Figure 5.32), is very common on soft bottoms at depths of 30 to 50 meters. It is easily recognized by the toothed keel that runs the length of its back. It gets its common name from the thick shell that has discouraged its use as a commercial species. The shells of old individuals are sometimes encrusted with the acorn barnacle, *Balanus amphitrite amphitrite*.

Another creature frequently caught during trawling for commercial shrimp is the mantis shrimp, *Squilla empusa* (Figure 5.33). Unlike the penaeid shrimp, *Squilla* is dorso-ventrally flattened and armed with sharp spines on its telson and razorlike antennal scales. It lives on muddy and sandy bottoms and is

Figure 5.29. The sugar shrimp, *Parapenaeus longirostris*. (x 0.5)

Figure 5.30. The seabob, *Xiphopeneus krøyeri*. (x 0.5)

Figure 5.31. The shrimp, *Trachypeneus constrictus*. (x 1.8)

Figure 5.32. The rock shrimp, *Sicyonia dorsalis*. (x 0.8)

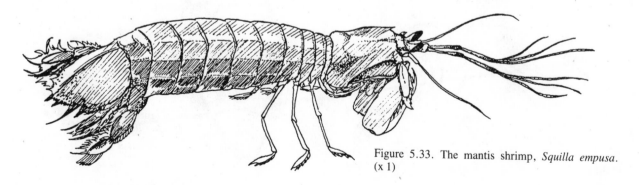

Figure 5.33. The mantis shrimp, *Squilla empusa*. (x 1)

Offshore Bottoms: The Shrimp Grounds   47

very efficient capturing small fish and shrimp from ambush with its large, raptorial legs. These legs, which are equipped with long spines for holding its prey, give *Squilla* the appearance of a praying mantis, from which it gets its common name. *Squilla* also orients chemotactically to food through receptors in its antennules. Although *Squilla* has very good vision, chemoreception helps it to locate food in turbid water. *Squilla* is less aggressive than most other mantis shrimps. When one approaches another, it vibrates its walking legs. They threaten one another by lowering the raptorial legs and placing the toothed portion of these legs on the substrate surface. *Squilla* rarely strike one another in aggressive encounters and usually walk away without a serious altercation. Mating occurs after a minimum of courtship behavior. The eggs are spawned after mating and are bundled into a large mass and carried by the female in her maxillipeds for 2 to 3 weeks until they hatch. During this time, the female occupies a burrow and rarely feeds.

Schools of two small caridean shrimps, *Leptochela serratorbita* (Figure 5.34) and *Ogyrides limicola* (Figure 5.35), are common in the northern Gulf, but are rarely recovered from commercial shrimp catches because the mesh of the nets used is too coarse. Both

species have a short rostrum without teeth, although *Ogyrides* has serrations on its carapace just behind the rostrum. This small, smooth rostrum distinguishes them from other caridean shrimps commonly encountered in the northern Gulf. *Ogyrides* has very long eyestalks, reminiscent of the sergestid shrimp *Acetes americana* (Figure 5.36). Although typically residents of water strata near the bottom, *Leptochela* and *Ogyrides* move freely through the water column and are occasionally caught in the surface plankton.

Crabs—Like Hermits and Frogs

Not all inhabitants of the offshore shrimp grounds are as cryptic as worms or burrowing crabs nor as elusive as shrimp. The persistent diver will encounter siphonal tubes maintained by large bivalves such as the quahog, *Mercenaria campechiensis*, the giant cockle, *Laevicardium robustum*, and the false angel wing, *Petricola pholadiformis*, as well as trails of gastropods such as the moon snail, *Natica canrena*, and the dwarf olive, *Olivella minuta* (Figure 5.37). Large shells of the horse conch, *Pleuroploca gigantea*, and various shells occupied by colorful hermit crabs are a fascinating part of this seascape.

The horse conch (Figure 3.22) is the largest marine snail in the northern Gulf, where its shell may attain a length of over 20 centimeters. Juveniles may be found on oil platforms, but the adults are restricted to the bottom. *Pleuroploca* is a predator of clams and other snails. Its shells and those of its gastropod prey are usually absorbed by one of the populations of large hermit crabs, such as *Petrochirus diogenes*, *Pagurus impressus*, *Paguristes puncticeps*, and *Dardanus fucosus*.

Pagurus impressus (Figure 5.38) is easily recognized by its flattened rust colored claws with serrated margins. Its antennae are yellow, and its eyestalks have patches of brown, blue, and scarlet. *Pagurus*

Figure 5.34. A caridean shrimp, *Leptochela serratorbita*. (x 3)

Figure 5.35. A caridean shrimp, *Ogyrides limicola*. (x 3)

Figure 5.36. A sergestid shrimp, *Acetes americana*. (x 3.5)

Figure 5.37. The dwarf olive, *Olivella minuta*. (x 5)

Figure 5.38. The hermit crab, *Pagurus impressus*. (x 0.7)

impressus occasionally wanders close to the beach, where it may be found around pier pilings or in the longshore troughs. *Paguristes puncticeps* (Figure 5.39) is also rust brown in color, but its claws are not nearly so flattened as those of *Pagurus impressus,* and unlike the latter species, are nearly equal in size. *Paguristes'* carapace is also covered with white spots. It is typically found offshore near reefs and the bases of oil platforms.

The bar-eyed hermit crab, *Dardanus fucosus,* derives its name from the horizontal black bar that transverses its bluish cornea. Its heavy purple claw is highlighted by blue warts, and its walking legs are accented by brownish-orange bands. This colorful crab spends most of its time beneath offshore oil platforms or on natural reefs, but seldom ventures near the shore in the northern Gulf.

The frog crab, *Raninoides louisianensis* (Figure 5.40), obtained its common name from its general appearance and the frog-like posture that it assumes. It typically rests on the sea floor with its anterior ends raised as if resting on the claws. Frog crabs usually partially bury themselves, similar to mole crabs.

The offshore mole crab, *Albunea paretii* (Figure 5.41), is readily distinguished from its littoral relative,

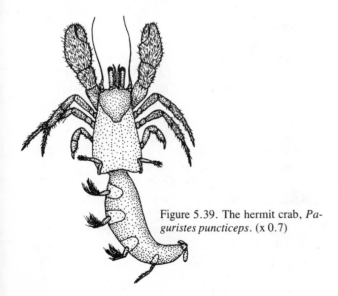

Figure 5.39. The hermit crab, *Paguristes puncticeps*. (x 0.7)

Lepidopa websteri (Figure 3.6), by its narrow, triangular eyestalks and tapering carapace. *Lepidopa* has broad eyestalks and a broad, squarish carapace. *Albunea* may be found near beaches inhabited by other mole crabs, but it is the predominant species in deeper water. Like its kin, it uses its hind legs to burrow into the sand backwards, leaving only a portion of its head and its very setose antennae extended above the surface. *Albunea's* antennae form a tube which permits a current of water to be drawn over its gills and filtering mouthparts.

Unlike many of its relatives, the longheaded porcelain crab, *Euceramus praelongus* (Figure 5.42), prefers a free-living existence among the shell rubble or coarse sand grains characteristic of submarine ridges and some beaches. Its cylindrical carapace gives it the appearance of a mole crab, but it lacks the spade-like telson and feathery antennae typically

Figure 5.40. The frog crab, *Raninoides louisianensis*. (x 1.2)

Figure 5.41. The offshore mole crab, *Albunea paretii*. (x 1.5)

Figure 5.42. The longheaded porcelain crab, *Euceramus praelongus*. (x 1.5)

found on mole crabs. The dull greenish color of *Euceramus'* carapace is often broken by fine gray or purple lines.

Another animal preferring coarse sediments is the amphipod *Batea cartharinensis* (Figure 5.43). Its large rectangular eyes and the serrated posterior edge of its third abdominal plate help to distinguish this species from other subtidal amphipods, including *Synchelium americanum* (Figure 5.44), *Ampelisca abdita* (Figure 5.45), and *Corophium acherusicum*. The latter three species generally prefer fine sediments. *Synchelidium* also has a relatively large eye, but it is located very close to its small, hooked rostrum. It is unusual among amphipods in that its first pair of claws are subchelate but its second pair are chelate. Its short, setose antennae are contrasted by its very long last walking legs. *Ampelisca* is easily recognized by its two pairs of small eyes. It lives in a long, narrow tube.

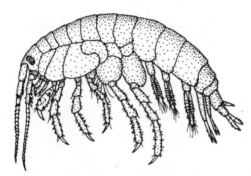

Figure 5.43. The amphipod *Batea cartharinensis*. (x 8)

Figure 5.44. The amphipod *Synchelium americanum*. (x 8)

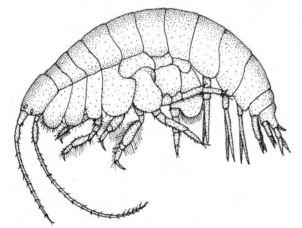

Figure 5.45. The amphipod *Ampelisca abdita*. (x 8)

Another tube-dwelling amphipod, *Corophium* has a body whose slimness is emphasized by its lack of large coxal plates. Its stout antennae flank the blunt projections bearing its eyes.

Creatures to Entice the Sea Lover

The horseshoe crab, *Limulus polyphemus* (Figure 5.46), is one of the most ancient and exotic marine animals in the Gulf. It is commonly encountered in the eastern Gulf in the spring when it moves inshore to spawn. In the western Gulf its distribution is apparently limited to the coast of Yucatan and to Galveston Bay, where it has been accidentally introduced. *Limulus* is not actually a crab at all, but is related to the extinct trilobites of ancient seas. Unlike true crabs, it lacks mandibles and must chew its food, consisting primarily of worms and mollusks, with the bases of its walking legs. Its long, rigid tail is used for balance and as an aid in burrowing. Females, which are much larger than the males, deposit their eggs in holes in the sand. The young hatch out in midsummer and swim off into deeper water, where they grow to adulthood in time for the following spring's migration.

The shovelnose or Spanish lobster, *Scyllarides nodifer* (Figure 5.47), has been tasted by relatively few Gulf coast residents. Although it reaches a sufficiently large size and its flesh is reportedly flavorful, it is not sufficiently abundant nor does it dwell close enough to shore to inspire harvesting on a commercial scale. Those individuals that are snared in shrimp trawls are usually eaten on board by the fishermen or taken home to their families. This colorful lobster is more flattened than the familiar New England lobster and has short, stout claws held close to its body. *Scyllarides* is brownish yellow with touches of red marking the carapace edges and many of the numerous tubercles on it's shell. Its yellow underside offsets its red and purple banded legs.

Several brittle stars live on the shrimp grounds. *Hemipholis elongata* (Figure 5.48) typically has a mottled gray and white body, or disc, and banded arms. Each of its 5 arms has a pattern of 4-8 dark segments alternating with 1-2 light segments. Each arm segment bears 3 conical spines on each side. *Micropholis atra* (Figure 5.49) resembles *Hemipholis* in that it is gray or dull lavender in color and has 5 arms bearing 6 conical spines per segment. However, its arms are not banded and its disc appears inflated or swollen. The scales on the upper surface of its disc are much larger than those on the lower surface, which extend slightly around the margin of the upper surface. Several of the scales on the disc's upper surface are darker than the others, giving the disc a somewhat mottled appearance, but less so than in *Hemipholis*.

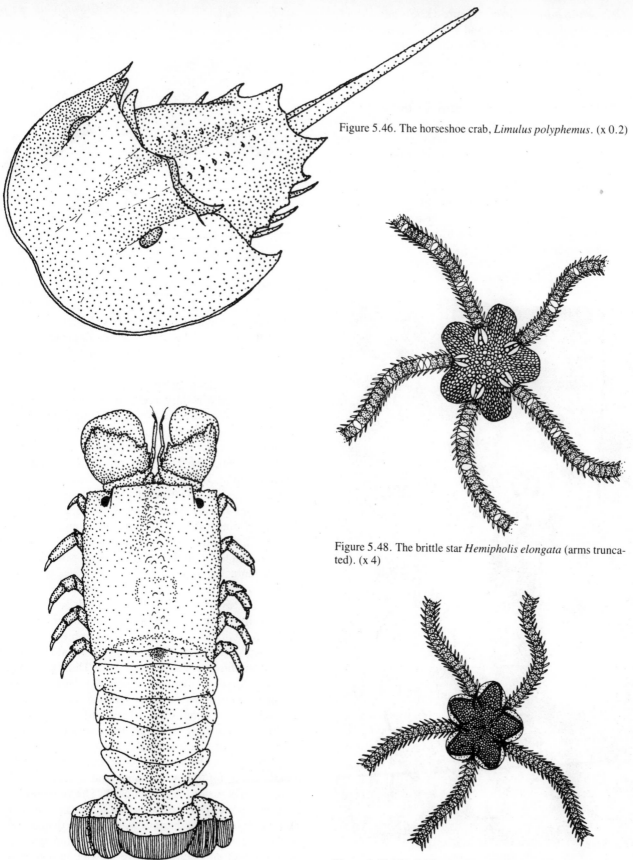

Figure 5.46. The horseshoe crab, *Limulus polyphemus*. (x 0.2)

Figure 5.48. The brittle star *Hemipholis elongata* (arms truncated). (x 4)

Figure 5.47. The Spanish lobster, *Scyllarides nodifer*. (x 0.2)

Figure 5.49. The brittle star *Micropholis atra* (arms truncated). (x 4)

Ophiophragmus moorei (Figure 5.50) has closely spaced bands on its arms and a row of spines around the margin of its disc. It is also rather drably colored. This species often extends into shallow water, where it can be found on sand bars in association with sand dollars.

Brittle stars typically lay buried in the sand with only the tips of their arms exposed. They shun light, and if exposed, they usually move away or bury themselves with a rowing action of two arms. The arm tips are often waved over the sand surface and grasp food particles encountered, which are transported to the mouth by podia or by retraction of the arm. Large pieces of decaying flesh may be sensed 10-20 centimeters away, stimulating the brittle star to unbury itself to reach its food.

Figure 5.50. The brittle star *Ophiophragmus moorei* (arms truncated). (x 4)

The Elusive Octopus

The cephalopod, *Octopus vulgaris* (Figure 5.51), occurs offshore. It inhabits crevices, large shells, or empty cans and is nocturnal in its habits. *Octopus* has a larger brain than any other invertebrate and can learn to discriminate among objects of different sizes and shapes for a reward and can retain the memory for at least three weeks. Along the underside of its eight legs, *Octopus* has two rows of suckers which can grasp objects securely. Its mouth lies in the center of the web of tentacles. The eyes are well developed and image-forming. When orienting to its prey the octopus only uses one eye. In estimating the distance of the object it raises and lowers its body. An octopus stalks its prey by gliding over the bottom and stopping within 15 or 20 centimeters of it. It then gathers itself together and leaps on the prey, trapping it beneath the web of tentacles.

Octopus exhibits a variety of colors and can change the surface texture of its skin. It responds to the color of its environment and exhibits the same color changes even when blinded. This behavior is protective; when the octopus is moving and changing colors at the same time, it confuses potential predators. During mating the male octopus deposits a spermatophore in the female's mantle cavity. This capsule breaks open, releasing the spermatozoa, which enter the oviduct and fertilize the eggs. The eggs are attached in strings to the roof of the octopus' burrow. As many as 150,000 eggs may be produced over a week's time. The female cares for them, cleaning and aerating them with spurts of water from her siphon. The young hatch in approximately 6 weeks, when they are nearly 1 millimeter long. The diminutive octopuses then spend weeks or months in the realm of the plankton and settle to the bottom when they have grown to a length of 5 millimeters or more.

Figure 5.51. The common octopus, *Octopus vulgaris*. (x 0.5)

The Bay Shore: Salt Marshes

Stands of the cordgrass, *Spartina alterniflora*, are a prominent feature of the bay shore. Many animals seek refuge on and among its sturdy stalks during tidal highs and daylight hours (Figure 6.1). One of the most abundant animals in this habitat is the marsh periwinkle, *Littorina irrorata* (Figure 6.2), a small yellow-brown snail which grows to a height of 2.3 centimeters. Faint lines on the shell, similar to the venation of the *Spartina* leaves, and the shape of its shell, reminiscent of a bent leaf, effectively camouflage it when viewed from above. *Littorina* climbs the *Spartina* stalks to escape the rising tide and while on the stalk secretes mucous around the perimeter of its shell lip. This permits the snail to withdraw into its shell and prevent desiccation by closing the aperture with the operculum carried on the back of its foot. When the tide recedes, the snail descends the stalk and crawls about on the mud, grazing on plant matter and other detritus as it glides along. This snail has a bipedal foot, i.e. the foot is divided into left and right halves which are alternately extended and contracted for locomotion.

Like most other prosobranch snails, *Littorina's* sexes are separate, and reproduction is accomplished by internal fertilization. Unlike most prosobranchs, *Littorina* releases its eggs into the water in single capsules. These planktonic eggs develop into trochophore larvae within the capsules and hatch as free-swimming veliger larvae. During this stage, small shells are developed as they transform into miniature adults, settling on the nearest *Spartina* stalks. During the summer and early fall months many young snails are present, but not all survive to adulthood due to physical hazards and predation by stone crabs.

If you look closely around the bases of the *Spartina* stalks, you may find fragments of shells of *Littorina*,

Figure 6.1. The salt marsh community: the hermit crab, *Clibanarius vittatus;* the fiddler crab, *Uca rapax;* the marsh periwinkle, *Littorina irrorata;* the horn shell, *Cerithidea pliculosa;* the pulmonate snail, *Melampus bidentatus;* and the amphipod, *Gammarus mucronatus.*

other gastropods and clams. These fragments are remnants of meals of the stone crab, *Menippe mercenaria*. These formidable crabs have massive, strong claws which are capable of cracking open clams, snails and hermit crab shells. They live in short burrows, excavated among the *Spartina* roots, usually open at both ends. *Menippe* is not as pugnacious as the blue

Figure 6.2. The marsh periwinkle, *Littorina irrorata*. (x 1.5)

Figure 6.3. The horn shell, *Cerithidea pliculosa*. (x 1.5)

crab and will withdraw into its burrow and wedge itself against the walls when disturbed.

Another snail, *Cerithidea pliculosa* (Figure 6.3), is common on the mud at the bases of the *Spartina* stalks. This turret-shaped snail has a thickened lip which forms a small, whitish ridge (or varix) on the shell as the snail grows. Populations of *Cerithidea* on Galveston Island are heavily parasitized by a number of trematodes. The cercariae of these parasites attack the gonad and hepatopancreas of the snail. Parasitism of the hepatopancreas probably results in impaired digestion; parasitism of the gonad impairs reproduction. A snail whose gonad is parasitized may grow to an abnormally large size since the energy usually allotted to reproduction is instead shunted into growth. *Cerithidea* grazes on the filamentous algae that grow on the mud at the base of the grass stalks.

Mussels and Worms in the Mud

At the roots of the *Spartina* growing in less saline parts of the bay and near the mouth of small creeks, clumps of the ribbed mussel, *Geukensia demissa granosissima* (Figure 6.4) may be found. Like most mussels, *Geukensia* anchors itself in the substrate with the aid of a heavy byssus; adults are usually burrowed

up to their siphons in the mud. Like the foot of the pen shell *Atrina,* the foot of *Geukensia* is greatly reduced. Though the young crawl freely until locating their kind and attaching, adults are relatively stationary as they have small feet and are only capable of feeble movements. This mussel is eurythermal, surviving temperatures from −22°C to 40°C; and euryhaline, surviving salinities from 5‰ to 100‰ and osmotically conforming in waters of 9‰ to 43‰. When *Geukensia* is exposed during low tide in the summer, the evaporative cooling of the wet mud reduces the mussel's temperature by as much as 5°C to 10°C. Frequently, the valves gape when the mussel is exposed, cooling the body by allowing water to evaporate from the tissues. *Geukensia* is photosensitive and, as a possible predator defense, responds to shadows by closing its valves both when submerged and exposed. In some areas, raccoons prey upon *Geukensia.*

Reproduction occurs in the spring, with the number of recruits to the populations being greatest in March and April. The shell grows throughout the year, especially in small and medium-sized individuals, though growth is most rapid during the warm months. It takes approximately two years for a young mussel to reach maturity. The greatest mortality occurs during the summer and fall, with virtually no population losses during the winter. The smallest *Geukensia* suffer the greatest mortality throughout the year.

One of the most common polychaetes in the muddy sand of the salt flats is *Laeonereis culveri,* which ranges in color from pinkish-red to yellowish-green. Because it burrows rather deeply in the mud, it is relatively resistant to short periods of low salinity and extreme temperatures as well as droughts. However, after prolonged periods of rain, many *Laeonereis* may be found exposed on the mud surface, relatively immobile due to osmotic stress.

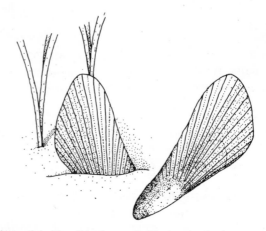

Figure 6.4. The ribbed mussel, *Geukensia demissa granosissima* (x 0.5)

Figure 6.5 The fiddler crab, *Uca rapax*. (x 2)

Fiddler Crabs and More Fiddler Crabs

The fiddler crab, *Uca* (Figure 6.5), is one of the most common crabs in the salt marsh. The common name of this genus of crabs refers to the oversized claw of the male; females can be recognized by their equal-sized small claws. The male uses his large claw mainly in social interactions. In contrast to subtidal crabs such as *Callinectes* and *Arenaeus,* semiterrestrial crabs rely less on chemical clues to find suitable mates. Thus, in most terrestrial species, visual and acoustic signals are highly developed as communicative devices. Male *Uca* attract females by waving the major cheliped in a certain pattern and producing sounds by tapping the ground and rubbing their legs together. Once having attracted a female, a male without a burrow mates with her on the surface. A male with a burrow entices the female into the burrow and mates with her there. As with other semiterrestrial crabs, mating occurs with the female's carapace hard. This adaptation not only reduces the chance of mechanical injury but also reduces the risk of dehydration.

A female *Uca* carries the eggs beneath her abdomen and releases the larvae at the water's edge. The larvae undergo five zoeal stages and a megalops stage, metamorphosing into an adultlike form as they settle on the shore. They then pass through five crablike stages before assuming the adult form completely. Fiddlers form very large colonies with the younger crabs usually living closer to the water's edge than older individuals.

The depth of the burrows of these crabs depends upon the water level within the sand. The upper portion of the burrow is usually straight, extending down at a steep angle for the first 30 centimeters or so. It then abruptly angles down, terminating in a small chamber at the water table. This chamber is usually partially filled with water. As high tide approaches, *Uca* plugs the burrow entrance with packed sand and spends high tide sitting in the chamber. When the tide recedes, the fiddler crab emerges from his burrow, feeds or attends to other business. Burrows in current use may be immediately recognized by small sand pellets around the entrance.

Uca usually feeds by sifting through a "clawful" of sand with its mouthparts for edible matter. Only the small claw of the male is used in feeding, though the female employs both. The sand surface is scraped and a dab is passed between the outermost mouthparts (third maxillipeds). Water from the gill chambers floods the mouth cavity, floating the lighter edible particles which are then caught by setae on the mouthparts and held by capillary action of the water. The unsuitable material drops to the bottom of the buccal cavity. Those species which feed in sand have more sorting setae on their mouthparts than those which feed in fine silty mud. Since water is necessary for feeding and branchial water is used in the process *Uca* must periodically refill its gill chambers, even though some of the water is recycled. As *Uca* sifts through continuously augmented mouthsful, a small drop of sand begins to form at the bottom of the mouthparts. When it grows to "pellet"size, it either drops to the ground or is wiped away with a claw. *Uca* also scavenges from beached fish and other dead animals. During low tides, especially at night, they emerge in hordes to feed and wet their gills at the water's edge. At this time, the less fleet-footed may fall prey to wading birds and *Callinectes* lurking in the shallows.

Figure 6.6. Major chelipeds and carapaces of male fiddler crabs (A) *Uca subcylindrica* (body shown in profile) (B) *Uca panaceae* (body shown in profile) (C) *Uca spinicarpa* (D) *Uca rapax* and (E) *Uca longisignalis*.

The color of *Uca* differs during daylight and nighttime. During the day, the dark pigment spots (melanophores) are dispersed and the white chromatophores (leucophores) are contracted so that *Uca* is dark in color. At night, conversely, the melanophores are contracted and the leucophores are dispersed, giving *Uca* a light color. The change in carapace color is an endogenous rhythm for crabs kept in total darkness will exhibit the same color changes as those under natural conditions. However, crabs kept in total light soon lose the rhythmical color change, indicating that the endogenous rhythm is influenced by photoperiod. Thus, crabs whose burrows are closer to the shore are submerged for longer periods, causing them to exhibit a slightly different color rhythm than crabs whose burrows are more supratidal and therefore submerged for shorter periods of time.

Of the 59 species of this genus that are recognized in the world, six species occur on the northwestern Gulf coast: *Uca subclindrica, Uca longisignalis, Uca spinicarpa, Uca rapax,* a western Gulf form of *Uca pugilator* which has recently been named *Uca panaceae* (Salmon, in press), and *Uca minax* (Figure 6.6). The last species, however, is a brackish-water form that is seldom found west of the Mississippi Delta. The males of the other species may be distinguished by the following characteristics; unfortunately, females of these species are less distinct.

Key to the Fiddler Crabs of the Northwestern Gulf Coast

1. If there is a presence of tubercles on the palm of the major chela refer to statement 3.
   In the absence of tubercles on the palm of the major chela refer to statement 2.
2. Carapace in lateral view cylindrical; abdomen of male broad .... *Uca subcylindrica* (in the Laguna Madre only in Texas; ranges to Mexico)
   Carapace in lateral view more flattened than cylindrical; abdomen of
   male narrower .... *Uca panaceae*
3. Spine present on inner median ridge of major cheliped carpus (turn claw upward to see it), tubercles on palm of major chela in
   right angle .... *Uca spincarpa* (ranges from west coast of Florida to Mexico)
   If there is no spine present on inner face of carpus of major cheliped, tubercles on palm not in right angle refer to statement 4.
4. Rostrum (carapace margin between eyes) squarish; red chromatophores present, especially on walking

legs and carapace; merus of walking legs not very setose .... *Uca rapax*
(ranges from Gulf of Mexico to Brazil)
Rostrum rounded; no red chromatophores; walking legs setose .... *Uca longisignalis*
(brackish to freshwater; not in Laguna Madre; ranges from the west coast of Florida to Brownsville, Texas)

Life in the Marsh Debris

Sesarma reticulatum and *Sesarma cinereum* (Figure 6.7), two other species of small crabs, also inhabit the marsh. *Sesarma reticulatum* lives in large communal burrows in the muddy part of the marsh, emerging during midtide to feed on the oldest, outermost leaves of the *Spartina* or any *Uca* it can catch. Their burrows are approximately 70 centimeters deep and usually filled with water. *Sesarma reticulatum* can be distinguished from *Sesarma cinereum* by the presence of a second tooth on the front side of the former's carapace (Figure 6.8). It is more robust than *Sesarma cinereum*, though less active. This is partially due to the greater gill area of *Sesarma cinereum*. The wood crab, *Sesarma cinereum*, lives high in the marsh in abandoned bird nests and under debris. Like *Uca*, they are primarily nocturnal in their habits and exhibit a color change rhythm. A female may carry from 5,000 to 13,000 eggs at a time and may breed up to five times during her lifetime.

Figure 6.7. The wood crab, *Sesarma cinereum*. (x 1.5)

Figure 6.8. Carapace of *Sesarma cinereum* (A) and *Sesarma reticulatum* (B). (x 1.5)

Figure 6.9. The pulmonate snail, *Melampus bidentatus*. (x 2)

Another supralittoral animal found in similar shaded refuges is the pulmonate snail, *Melampus bidentatus* (Figure 6.9). Lacking gills, this snail respires across its highly vascularized mantle cavity wall and will drown during prolonged submergence. During their six-week reproductive period, occurring from late May to early July, the snails' behavior is synchronized with the lunar cycle and the occurrence of biweekly high tides. These hermaphroditic snails aggregate at this time and mate. Oviposition occurs at each spring tide (every two weeks) over a period of four days. Over all these periods, each individual deposits approximately 40 egg masses; each egg mass contains an average of 850 eggs.

The *Melampus* eggs are deposited in a single continuous strand enclosed in two tubular gelatinous layers. The eggs develop in 10-11 days and are protected from desiccation during this time by tidal deposition of detritus. The eggs hatch into veligers at the next spring tide and enter the plankton where they spend two to six weeks. Settlement of the young also occurs on a high spring tide. Growth is slow during the winter and greatest in the spring and summer. *Melampus* attain sexual maturity at approximately 5 millimeters in length and live for three to four years, reaching a maximum length of 10.5 millimeters. *Melampus* is most active at night, during the morning and evening twilight hours and on cloudy, sultry days. On warm, sunny days it usually takes refuge under debris or in *Uca* burrows. Its diet consists chiefly of diatoms and other algae, though it also consumes tissues of higher plants and decayed animal matter.

Gammarus mucronatus (Figure 6.10) is a large, reddish-brown amphipod that utilizes the debris trapped in the marsh for both food and shelter. Ovigerous females occur from April to September. This species ranges from the Gulf of St. Lawrence to the Gulf of Mexico in a variety of estuarine habitats.

Figure 6.10. The amphipod, *Gammarus mucronatus*. (x 5)

Figure 6.11. The great land crab, *Cardisoma guanhumi*. (x 0.5)

Land crabs

One of the largest crabs living along the Texas coast is the great land crab, *Cardisoma guanhumi* (Figure 6.11). Adult males may weigh 500 grams at carapace widths of 10-11 centimeters. These crabs have inflated epibranchial chambers which aid in respiratory exchange by increasing the volume of air to which the gills are exposed. Although *Cardisoma* can survive three days without water, they frequently moisten their gills with the ground water that wells up in the bottom of their burrows. These herbivorous crabs burrow in muddy sand at varying depths, depending on the water table, and may be found up to eight kilometers from the sea along canals and irrigation ditches. *Cardisoma* also commonly burrows beneath mangroves growing along bays.

The upper part of the *Cardisoma* burrow extends at a 25° to 50° angle from the surface, then descends steeply to the water table, increasing slightly in width. At the bottom, the burrow is expanded into a chamber one to two liters in volume. Dirt is excavated with the large claw and carried to the surface held between the major cheliped and the body. During the winter, the burrow mouth is plugged and the crab remains below the surface. New burrows may be constructed in the summer months.

Juveniles are tan or brown in color and usually weighs five grams or less. Maturing crabs have purple spots on carapace and weigh up to 40 grams. The adults are bluish-gray with whitish chelipeds. Females may exhibit the adult coloration before they reach sexual maturity. Crabs weighing 80-90 grams are usually mature. The spawning season extends from June or early July to December with a peak in October and November. The number of eggs carried per female ranges from 200,000 to 700,000 though the average number borne is 370,000. The freshly attached eggs are black and turn brown over the 10-12 days of development. When ready to spawn the females mass and migrate to the sea, which appears to occur on a bimonthly lunar rhythm. The larvae are released by fanning the abdomen and they spend approximately five months in the plankton before metamorphosing and returning to land. In Central America, *Cardisoma* is an important protein source for lower economic groups. In the United States, man is less a predator than raccoons which appear to be an important consumer of *Cardisoma*.

The black land crab, *Gecarcinus lateralis* (Figure 6.12) is another terrestrial crab found in this area. It is only found in the extreme southern portion of Texas where it constructs burrows on the back side of the dunes. It is a nocturnal feeder and thus is not often encountered.

Figure 6.12. The black land crab, *Gecarcinus lateralis*. (x 1)

Invisible Grass Shrimp

Returning to the water's edge, we can find some animals that frequent the *Spartina* but also exist elsewhere in the bay. The transparent grass shrimp, *Palaemonetes pugio* (Figure 6.13) and *Palaemonetes vulgaris*, take refuge from predators among the *Spartina* stalks at high tide. Young commercial shrimp, such as *Penaeus aztecus,* may also share this refuge. These genera represent the two major groups of shrimp, Caridea and Penaeidea, respectively. These groups may be distinguished in the field by the shape of the tail. Caridea are often nicknamed "broken-back" shrimp because the covering of the fourth abdominal segment is capped over the fifth segment. Thus, the tail of a Caridean shrimp will have a noticeable hump when viewed from the side, in contrast to the smooth line of the tail of a penaeid shrimp.

Palaemonetes, like *Panaeus,* is a scavenger. These shrimp are most abundant in areas ranging in salinity from 10‰ to 20‰. Males and females may be distinguished by the shape of the second pair of abdominal appendages modified as copulatory organs in the male. Female *Palaemonetes* attach their fertilized eggs to their pleopods. The eggs are aerated by the rhythmic beating of the pleopods and kept free of

Figure 6.13. The grass shrimp, *Palaemonetes pugio.* (x 2)

detritus by frequent cleaning. The number of eggs carried per female depends upon her size, but ranges from 100 to 700. Spawning occurs in July and October. Those young spawned in the summer grow to maturity in two to three months; those spawned in the fall require four to six months. Grass shrimp live for one year, though hapless individuals may be consumed by redfish and speckled trout.

The Bay Shore: Mud Flats

Extensive portions of the shallow Gulf Coast bays are covered by only a few inches of water at low tide and may be exposed during extreme low tides and northers. These mud flats are too low for the development of salt marshes and, far from being flat, they are finely sculptured by currents, waves and burrowing animals. Like the sandy beach, the mud flat is a habitat best suited for burrowing species or very motile species. The substrate varies depending upon the location, being somewhat sandier near the passes and in channels cut by currents. This in turn influences the fauna that we find on the mud flat.

Razors, Jackknives and Boring Clams

Two species of razor clam, so called because of their elongate shape, are common burrowers in sandy mud. The stout razor, *Tagelus plebeius* (Figure 7.1), is a deposit feeder like the tellin clams. *Tagelus* lives in habitats in which the salinity may be less than 10‰ or greater than 30‰. However, it lives in deep burrows in which the variation in salinity is not nearly so great. The stout razor has numerous enemies, including the drill, *Thais haemastoma;* the blue crab, *Callinectes sapidus;* the hermit crab, *Clibanarius vittatus;* and various shorebirds. The shells of dead *Tagelus* often rise to the mud surface where they stand erect like small monuments.

The slimmer, more elongate jackknife clam, *Ensis minor* (Figure 7.2), is a filter-feeder. Despite its fragile appearance, this greenish clam has a powerful foot with which it can dig itself into the mud in seconds. The foot extends down into the sediment and swells with water, widening the hole. The tip of the foot then anchors itself at the bottom of the hole and contracts,

yanking the rest of the clam after it. *Ensis* is a favorite prey of the whelk *Busycon contrarium,* which may nearly bury itself in search of this slender clam. *Ensis* differs from *Tagelus* in that the hinge, or point of attachment, of its valves is located at the end rather than in the middle of its shell.

Another burrowing clam usually found in stiff mud is the fragile angel wing, *Cyrtopleura costata* (Figure 7.3), a relative of the boring clams often found in wood or oyster shell. This clam burrows 30 centimeters or more beneath the surface, depending on its size. Its long, fused siphons protrude about 1 centimeter above the mouth of the burrow and circulate water and suspended matter below to the gills. The clam cannot completely close its shell nor withdraw the siphons into the shell, thus it is susceptible to extremes of temperature and salinity. The musculature

Figure 7.1. The stout razor, *Tagelus plebeius*. (x 1)

Figure 7.2. The jackknife clam, *Ensis minor*. (x 1.5)

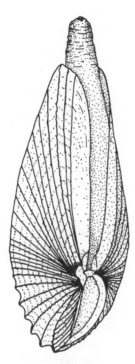

Figure 7.3. The angel wing, *Cyrtopleura costata*. (x 1)

shells is covered by a chocolate brown periostracum and its smooth surface is broken only by thin growth lines. *Rangia* is found from Chesapeake Bay to Texas. It reproduces once per year (in the spring) in the northern part of its range and twice per year (spring and autumn) in the Gulf of Mexico.

The dwarf surf clam, *Mulinia lateralis* (Figure 7.5), lives in clayey mud in the bays. It is tolerant of a wide range of salinities; hence it is common in both low salinity bays and the hypersaline lagoons, such as the Laguna Madre. *Mulinia's* small, cream-colored shell is nearly triangular in shape. This abundant clam is an important food item for bottom-feeding fish.

The constricted macoma, *Macoma constricta* (Figure 7.6), is a common deposit feeding bivalve in northwestern Gulf Coast bays. It is about 4-6 centimeters long and is very tolerant of temperature and

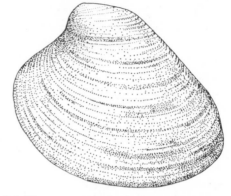

Figure 7.4. The common rangia, *Rangia cuneata*. (x 1)

Figure 7.5. The dwarf surf clam, *Mulinia lateralis*. (x 2.5)

holding the valves together is quite weak and it depends upon the stiff mud for support. If you are patient enough to carefully dig up a *Cyrtopleura* intact, it will survive longer if you tie a string around the valves. Old *Cyrtopleura* shells are often found projecting upright from the mud. The gaping valves of these shells provide a refuge for small mud crabs, such as *Rithropanopeus harrisii* and *Panopeus herbstii*.

Clams for Food, Roads, and Barter

With the possible exception of the oyster, the common rangia, *Rangia cuneata* (Figure 7.4), is often the most common bivalve in the low salinity bays. A truly estuarine species, it is found well into the mouths of the rivers and bayous and grows to its maximum size in brackish water. *Rangia* shells have been used as a road surfacing material in areas where they are particularly abundant. The outer surface of these thick

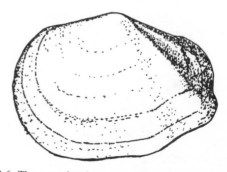

Figure 7.6. The constricted macoma, *Macoma constricta*. (x 1)

Figure 7.7. The southern quahog, *Mercenaria campechiensis texana.* (x 0.8)

salinity extremes. *Macoma* buries itself in the mud by rocking its shell back and forth so that it cuts into the mud. A smaller relative, *Macoma mitchelli,* is found in the mud in brackish water near the mouths of rivers.

The southern quahog, *Mercenaria campechiensis texana* (Figure 7.7), seems an unlikely mud flat resident. Its heavy shell is reminiscent of clams living in more turbulent waters. This clam lives in soft mud 3-4 centimeters beneath the surface. It is closely related to the Atlantic quahog, *Mercenaria mercenaria,* which is commonly used in clam chowder. The shell of the southern species lacks the purple border present on the valves of the Atlantic quahog. The shells of the latter species were used as currency by Atlantic seaboard Indians. *Mercenaria campechiensis texana* frequently falls prey to large *Menippe* and *Callinectes,* as suggested by the shell fragments littering the grass flats at low tide. Young *Mercenaria* are also a common prey of whelks. Due to the lack of large waves and the heavy weight of *Mercenaria's* shell, this shell often remains on the mud flat long after the clam's death. Here it fills with mud and is frequently inhabited by a mud crab, a mud shrimp, or a ribbon worm.

15 millimeters wide and prefers sheltered locations—clam shells, oyster reefs, tin cans, and clumps of vegetation.

The common mud crab, *Panopeus herbstii* (Figure 7.9), can also be found in old *Mercenaria* shells or in tin cans on the mud flats. The area's largest mud crab, it grows to a width of 38 millimeters. It has a large tooth on the moveable finger of its large claw, which can be used to chip pieces off of the shells of small oysters and barnacles. The flat mud crab, *Eurypanopeus depressus* (Figure 7.10), is smaller than *Panopeus* (about 20 millimeters wide) and lacks the large tooth on its claw. It is usually mottled grayish-olive to dark olive brown in color and has a red spot on the concealed side of its claw. *Neopanope texana texana* (Figure 7.11) is a slightly larger mud crab (27 millimeters wide) that lacks both the tooth and the red spot on its claw.

The stone crab, *Menippe mercenaria,* is a member of the same family as the mud crabs and often shares their mud flat habitat. Small stone crabs live primarily in crevices on the jetties and oyster reefs, but large ones dig burrows on the mud flat and along the edge of the marsh. These burrows play an important role in

Mud Crabs and Mud Shrimp

The smallest mud crab living on the mud flat is *Rithropanopeus harrisii* (Figure 7.8). It can be distinguished from the other mud crabs and from small stone crabs by the pale tips of its claws; other similar crabs have black-tipped claws. It is usually less than

Figure 7.8. The mud crab, *Rithropanopeus harrisii.* (x 2)

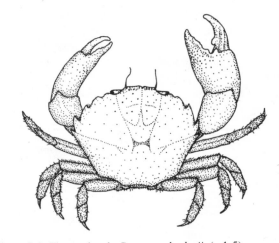

Figure 7.9. The mud crab, *Panopeus herbstii.* (x 1.5)

Figure 7.10. The flat mud crab, *Eurypanopeus depressus.* (x 1.5)

Figure 7.11. The mud crab, *Neopanope texana texana.* (x 1)

Figure 7.12. The mud shrimp, *Callianassa jamaicense louisianensis.* (x 2)

the ecology of the mud flat since they often contain most of the water left there at low tide. Mud crabs, hermit crabs, grass shrimp, snapping shrimp, worms and several species of fish may find shelter from the drying sun and foraging shorebirds in stone crab burrows. During cold weather *Menippe* may plug up the entrance to its burrow. Young *Menippe* often play dead when cornered and may autotomize legs that are caught. Old stone crabs occasionally carry the acorn barnacle, *Chelonibia patula,* on their carapaces.

The mud shrimp *Callianassa jamaicense louisianensis* (Figure 7.12) sometimes builds its burrow in mud that has collected in a large *Mercenaria* shell. It is a small, delicate shrimp with one oversized claw. *Callianassa* typically burrows into the mud near vegetation and sometimes shares its burrow with the small commensal crab *Pinnixa chaetopterana.*

Delicate Ribbon Worms

The ribbon worm or nemertean, *Cerebratulus lacteus* (Figure 7.13), is an inhabitant of the soft mud and can sometimes be found in the mud inside old clam shells or in abandoned tubes of the polychaete *Diopatra cuprea.* This pale yellow worm is a voracious predator on other worms and small crustaceans. *Cerebratulus* may reach lengths of over one meter on the East Coast, but it rarely grows that large on the Gulf Coast. It is sometimes called a proboscis worm because of its long proboscis that can be shot out to capture prey some distance away. The name ribbon worm applies to its long, slender, flattened body.

Figure 7.13. The ribbon worm, *Cerebratulus lacteus.* (x 4)

A bright red nemertean, *Micrura leidyi,* lives in the sandier sediment near the passes. *Micrura* may attain a length of 20 centimeters, but it is very fragile and thus difficult to obtain intact. It lacks eyespots and its anterior end is marked by a small, whitish mouth.

Figure 7.16. The common mud snail,
Nassarius vibex. (x 2)

Figure 7.14. A sand collar: the egg case of the moon snail, *Polinices.* (x 1)

Figure 7.17. The common Atlantic auger, *Terebra dislocata.*
(x 1.5)

Augers, Drills, and Moon Snails

The moon snail, *Polinices duplicatus,* which also inhabits the sandy beach, can be found gliding along just
below the surface, especially near the passes where the
substrate is somewhat sandy. These snails lay their
minute eggs in a capsule called a sand collar (Figure
7.14), in which the eggs are interspersed among sand
grains in a mucous matrix. *Polinices* has an enormous
foot, which expands to about twice the area of the
shell. This foot is expanded by an internal vascular
system; when the animal retracts into its shell, the
fluid is drained from this system and the foot is folded
into the shell.

A member of the naticid family, *Sinum perspectivum* (Figure 7.15), has a shell that is only partially
exposed. Its shell is usually called a baby's ear by shell
collectors, and it resembles a miniature abalone shell.
Sinum also burrows beneath the sand surface and is
highly modified for this habit. Unlike *Polinices* foot,
Sinum's foot is not retractible. *Sinum* glides through
the sand by muscular action, aided by a copious secretion of mucous.

The common mud snail, *Nassarius vibex* (Figure
7.16), is found along the bay edges and subtidally. It is
a scavenger with a highly developed chemoreceptive
capability. The shells of these little snails provide
homes for tiny hermit crabs that have recently settled
from the plankton.

The common Atlantic auger, *Terebra dislocata*
(Figure 7.17), can often be found near the passes. It
crawls just under the sand surface occasionally leaving
a bulge in the surface. For an unknown reason,
Terebra occasionally crawls out onto the surface in
large numbers, and its white shell is very conspicuous.
This carnivorous snail apparently has a venom which
it uses in the capture of its prey.

The oyster drill, *Thais haemastoma,* can be found in
great numbers during the spring breeding season lay-
ing eggs in capsules just beneath the waterline on
almost any available hard surface, such as pier pilings
and other *Thais.* These long, rectangular capsules turn
yellow if laid on surfaces which are left dry when the
tide recedes.

Hermit Crabs on the Bayshore

Three species of hermit crabs are common in the
bays: *Pagurus longicarpus* (Figure 7.18), *Pagurus
pollicaris* and *Clibanarius vittatus.* The latter is most
abundant and appears to be the most tolerant of water
temperature and salinity fluctuations. All three
species are scavengers, and they compete with one
another for suitable shells. *Pagurus* is frequently
found in shells encrusted with colonies of the hydroids
Hydractinia echinata (Figure 7.19) and *Podocoryne
selena. Clibanarius* appears unable to inhabit shells
encrusted with living colonies of these hydroids, whose

Figure 7.15. *Sinum perspectivum,* (A) live snail (x 1) and (B) ventral view of shell (x 1.5).

Figure 7.18. The hermit crab, *Pagurus longicarpus*. (x 1.5)

Figure 7.19. The commensal hydroid, *Hydractinia echinata*, with a magnification of the polyps. (x 1)

protective zooids seem to sting this hermit crab. The stinging zooids apparently do not harm *Pagurus*, either because *Pagurus* inhibits the firing of the nematocysts or because it is immune to the sting. Thus the less abundant *Pagurus* are afforded some protection from *Clibanarius* during shell fights. *Clibanarius*, easily recognized by its striped legs, is the most abundant intertidal hermit crab during the summer. In winter it migrates into the shallow subtidal zone where it aggregates and frequently buries itself in the mud. It is quite rare along the shore during January and February. The long-armed hermit crab, *Pagurus longicarpus*, has longer and more slender claws than does the thumb-clawed hermit crab, *Pagurus pollicaris*, whose short, flat claws can be used to plug the aperture of its shell when molested. Both species of *Pagurus* are more common nearshore during the winter when they apparently move into shallow water to breed since many of the females are carrying eggs at this time. *Pagurus longicarpus* is the most common species on the East Coast, where it is usually found nearshore during the summer and migrates into deeper water during the winter.

Another inhabitant of soft, sandy mud is the parchment tube worm, *Chaetopterus variopedatus* (Figure 7.20). This worm is a good example of modification of the parapodia and body segments to a tube-dwelling existence. It lives in a U-shaped tube with a parchmentlike lining with the ends protruding above the mud. *Chaetopterus* never leaves its tube to feed as do some predacious species, but filters plankton from the water by a unique method. Modified parapodia near the anterior of the worm secrete mucous along their interior margin; this mucous flows back to form a sack as a water current is set up in the tube by the fans (other modified parapodia). When it is full of food particles, this mucous sieve is formed into a bolus which is passed forward to the mouth by rows of cilia and swallowed. All of the similar segments on the posterior section of the body are nearly completely filled with gonad. *Chaetopterus* is a stenohaline species rarely found where the salinity drops below 20‰. Hence it is usually found near the passes. It is a volume regulating osmoconformer, meaning that it adjusts to salinity changes by swelling or shriveling until its internal salt concentration is nearly the same as that of its environment.

Chaetopterus frequently harbors a number of other animals in its tube. The crab, *Pinnixa chaetopterana*, is a common boarder; usually a male and a female can be found in the same tube. These elongate little crabs enter and leave the tube at will, biting a hole in the chimney if the end of the tube is too small. These crabs filter-feed by sweeping their very setose feeding legs (maxillipeds) through the water. The fringe of setae is then cleaned by the other mouthparts to collect the food. *Pinnixa* probably takes advantage of the water current in the *Chaetopterus* tube for its filter-feeding and thus does not steal food directly from its host.

The lugworm, *Arenicola cristata* (Figure 7.21), is one of the mud flat's more interesting residents. It lives in an L-shaped burrow consisting of a mucous-lined horizontal gallery and a vertical tail shaft. *Arenicola* is a thick, dark green worm with eleven pairs of reddish gills near the center of its body. Water is drawn down the tail shaft, bringing oxygen to the gills, and is then forced up through the sediment at the blind end of the gallery. As *Arenicola's* gallery is often located in the black, sulfide-rich sediment layers, the stream of fresh water results in the oxidation of the sediment, changing its color to yellow. The lugworm is a direct deposit-feeder, i.e. it swallows this oxidized sediment and digests any organic matter in it as it passes through the worm's gut. It then backs up the tail shaft to defecate, and its tail is most vulnerable to attacks by shorebirds. *Arenicola* is well adapted to low

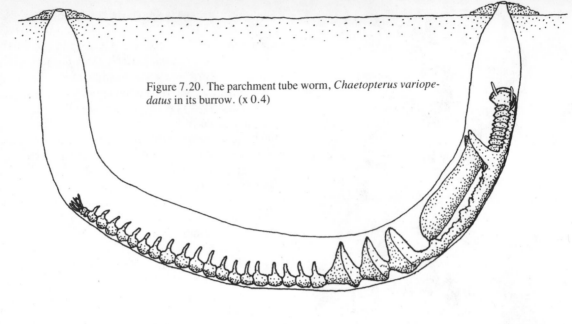

Figure 7.20. The parchment tube worm, *Chaetopterus variope-datus* in its burrow. (x 0.4)

Figure 7.21. The lugworm, *Arenicola cristata*. (x 1)

Figure 7.22. Anterior end of *Eteone heteropoda*. (x 25)

oxygen environments. If the tide stays out too long, *Arenicola* will retrieve bubbles of air from the surface and pass them to the gills. The gills can use atmospheric oxygen so long as they remain wet.

There are many other common species of polychaete worms in the bays, among which are *Eteone heteropoda*, (Figure 7.22), *Laeonereis culveri, Neanthes succinea* (Figure 7.23), *Ceratonereis irritabilis* (Figure 7.24), and *Capitella capitata floridana (Figure 5.10), Eteone* and *Capitella* lack jaws and are probably deposit-feeders. *Eteone* is a pale yellow or greenish worm about 50-90 millimeters long usually found intertidally in sandy mud. *Capitella* differs from the other species in that it has very few parapodia; thus except for its eyes it looks like a blood red earthworm. The red color is due to the blood which can be seen through its skin. *Capitella* is approximately 100-120 millimeters long and usually lives in vertical burrows in mud or fine sand. *Capitella* is often one of the first organisms to reinvade areas damaged by oil spills; thus its presence is occasionally interpreted as an indication of oil pollution.

Laeonereis, Neanthes, and *Ceratonereis* are all members of the family Nereidae. They are active predators equipped with a pair of horny jaws with

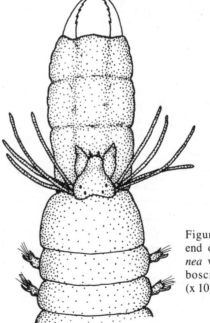

Figure 7.23. Anterior end of *Neanthes succinea* with extended proboscis showing jaws. (x 10)

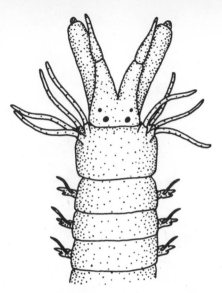

Figure 7.24. The head of a *Ceratonereis irritabilis*. (x 10)

teeth along their inner edges. *Neanthes* is the largest of these worms; it reaches a length of 190 millimeters. It is a cosmopolitan species and is found in a great variety of habitats: on pilings, among oysters, in sandy or muddy sediment, under stones and among barnacles. It is tolerant of a wide range of salinities from brackish water to marine water. *Laeonereis* is a very common species on mud flats and in salt marshes where it constructs deep vertical burrows. It is about 30 millimeters long and varies in color from pink to red to bright yellow to green. *Ceratonereis* has a light gray anterior region, a bluish mid region and a brass-colored posterior region, and the bases of its parapodia are green. It reproduces through a process known as epitoky. The posterior end of the body, which contains the gonads, differs markedly from the anterior end. As the gonads mature the worm transforms from a nonsexual individual, or atoke, into a sexual individual, or epitoke. The epitokes then swim up into the water. This activity is synchronized so that numerous epitokes enter the plankton at the same time. These swarms of epitokes release their gametes into the water where fertilization takes place.

Platynereis dumerilii (Figure 6.25) is another predacious nereid worm that is common nearshore. It constructs a pliable tube composed of several layers of fine threads held together by an adhesive secretion. Specialized anterior parapodia secrete the threads and adhesive. Bits of debris are often incorporated into the tube wall. Bundles of threads anchor the tube to the substratum—often a seagrass blade or old shell. Like most other nereids, *Platynereis* seldom tolerates direct contact with other worms, except during courtship,

and quickly chases intruders from its tube. Sense organs on the anterior cirri, palps, and tentacles are used to identify worms of other species or sex. Rapid biting thrusts of the proboscis accompany pursuit of unwelcome visitors to the burrow's exit.

Aggressive encounters between nereid worms are easily observed in sections of glass or clear plastic tubing. Introducing various combinations of species, sexes, or sizes into opposite ends of the tubing yields interesting behavioral experiments. A long-stemmed glass funnel can be used to manipulate stubborn worms. Try letting one of the worms make itself "at home" before adding its adversary.

Life in the Seagrass Meadow

Bays along the coasts of Alabama, Florida, and Texas are structured by underwater meadows of vascular plants generically known as seagrasses. Seagrasses have tropical affinities, and form lush beds at low latitudes. In the northern Gulf the erect blades, or turions, die back during the winter and are broken off by storm waves, leaving a live network of rhizoidal-roots to regenerate new turions in the spring.

Our most common species are the turtle grass, *Thalassia testudinum,* and the shoal grass, *Halodule wrightii* (Figure 7.25). As its name implies, shoal grass is often found in shallow water and may be exposed at low tide. Widgeon grass, *Ruppia maritima,* also inhabits shoal areas but prefers a lower salinity than that tolerated by *Halodule.*

Seagrasses help to stabilize the physical environment and provide cover for numerous small orga-

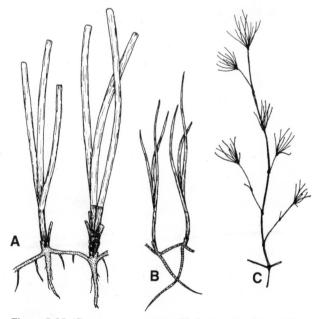

Figure 7.25. Common seagrasses, *Thalassia testudinum* (A), *Halodule wrightii* (B), and *Ruppia maritima* (C). (x 0.3)

nisms. Their meadows form nursery areas for major Gulf of Mexico shrimp and crab populations. Juvenile blue crabs and juvenile penaeid shrimp exploit the cover provided by these plants to pass the numerous molts required by rapid growth in early life. Each molt is accompanied by a vulnerable soft-shelled stage.

Juvenile pink, brown, and white shrimps share this habitat with several other species, some of which spend their entire lives in the meadow. Perhaps the most ubiquitous of these species is the broken-back shrimp, *Hippolyte pleuracantha* (Figure 7.26). *Hippolyte* is somewhat of a chameleon, ranging in color from a bright kelly green to a speckled reddish brown depending on the color of the grass to which it is clinging.

The arrow shrimp, *Tozeuma carolinensis* (Figure 7.27), is so named because of its long rostrum (the spine at the front of the carapace) and its elongated body. It too can match its color to its background by responses of color organs called chromatophores imbedded beneath its integument. In Florida *Tozeuma* is bluish purple on gorgonians of the same color and green on grass. Its ability to flatten itself against the grass blade also conceals its presence.

The snapping shrimp, *Alpheus heterochaelis* (Figure 7.28), is usually found under debris or in discarded cans within the grass beds. It prefers sheltered locations in quiet, shallow water and is sometimes common on oyster reefs. The major claw of this shrimp has a small disk on which a circular "hammer" closes when muscular tension reaches a release

Figure 7.28. The snapping shrimp, *Alpheus heterochaelis*. (x 1.5)

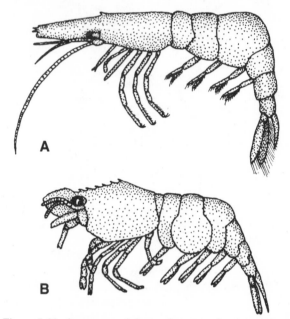

Figure 7.29. Sargassum shrimps, *Latreutes fucorum* (A) and *Latreutes parvulus* (B). (x 2.5)

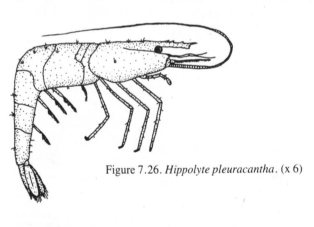

Figure 7.26. *Hippolyte pleuracantha*. (x 6)

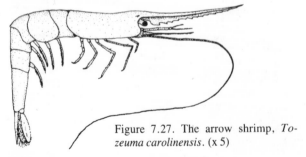

Figure 7.27. The arrow shrimp, *Tozeuma carolinensis*. (x 5)

point. The closure of this disk produces a loud pop, stunning small crustaceans which *Alpheus* feeds upon. Males and females are usually found together, the female being about twice the size of the male. Females carry their green eggs on their pleopods, as does *Palaemonetes*. *Alpheus* will do well in capitivity provided it is given a piece of pipe or small jar to hide in.

The grass shrimp, *Palaemonetes pugio* (Figure 6.13) and *Palaemonetes vulgaris,* are characteristic residents of seagrass meadows. The sargassum shrimps, *Latreutes parvulus* and *Latreutes fucorum* (Figure 7.29), are less common and may be occasional invaders rather than residents. *Latreutes fucorum* is typically brownish green or greenish yellow with white spots, but this pattern is quite variable in that this shrimp often blends well with its environment. *Latreutes parvulus* is much stockier than *Latreutes fucorum* and has a very short rostrum. It is also found associated with sponges in the eastern Gulf.

Figure 7.30. The hermit crab, *Pagurus annulipes*. (x 8)

Young blue crabs, mud crabs, *Neopanope texana texana* (Figure 7.11), spider crabs, *Libinia dubia* (Figure 3.45), and several hermit crab species are commonly seen in seagrass beds. The striped hermit crab, *Clibanarius vittatus* (Figure 2.8), is a common migrant in Texas, moving confidently between the meadow and the adjacent exposed sea floor under the protection of its borrowed shell. Minute hermit crabs, *Pagurus bonairensis* and *Pagurus annulipes* (Figure 7.30), are abundant in Florida seagrass meadows.

Dove snails, *Anachis semiplicata* (Figure 2.10), may be seen dangling from grass turions by slender mucous threads. Brittle stars, *Ophiothrix angulata* (Figure 8.22) and *Ophiactis savignyi* (Figure 8.21), are sometimes entangled around the plant bases, particularly in the eastern Gulf. Sediment within the meadow is often inhabited by phoronids, *Phoronis architecta* (Figure 5.7), and worms such as *Diopatra cuprea* (Figure 3.12), *Owenia fusiformis* (Figure 5.8) and *Polydora ligni*.

Clams and Scallops of the Grass Beds

The pale orange shells of *Lucina pectinata* (Figure 7.31) are a common sight on beaches near the passes and along the bay margins. This medium-sized bivalve is found in the grass flats but is not restricted to them. Occasionally a shell is found with the distinctive boring of a naticid snail (probably *Polinices duplicatus*), suggesting that *Lucina* is found in the more open areas

patrolled by this predator. *Lucina* is tolerant of a broad salinity range enabling it to exist in the hypersaline lagoons of South Texas as well as in the brackish bays of North Texas.

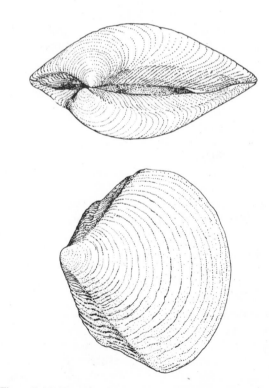

Figure 7.31. The thick lucine, *Lucina pectinata*. (x 1.3)

Figure 7.32. The cross-barred venus, *Chione cancellata*. (x 1)

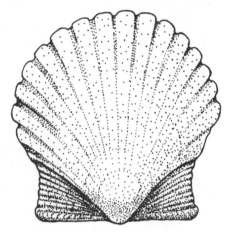

Figure 7.33. The bay scallop, *Argopecten irradians amplicostatus*. (x 1)

The whitish shell of the cross-barred venus, *Chione cancellata* (Figure 7.32), is characterized by its high, bladelike concentric ridges superimposed on numerous radial ribs, giving it a latticed appearance. These ridges are often curved toward the apex so they offer less resistance during burrowing than they do to removal of the clam from the sediment by currents or by predators such as the whelks *Busycon* spp. When disturbed, *Chione* begins to wander usually leaving a telltale furrow in the sand. It is usually found in the upper 15 centimeters of sand and is usually more abundant in the grass than in bare areas.

The bay scallop, *Argopecten irradians amplicostatus* (Figure 7.33), is another bivalve that is found both on the grass flats and on the adjacent bay bottom. It is unusual among bivalves in that it moves by swimming in short spurts just above the bottom. This is accomplished by opening its valves and then quickly closing them, forcing out a stream of water which propels the scallop in the opposite direction. The margin of the mantle has numerous eyes among a fringe of short tentacles. These eyes are very sensitive to sudden changes in light intensity, so a passing shadow may cause the scallop to take flight.

The Inconspicuous Cucumber

The sea cucumber, *Thyone mexicana* (Figure 7.34), is a sluggish member of the fauna that is found in and around the grass flats. It is rather small (2-3 centimeters long) as sea cucumbers go, so it is easily confused with a small rock or bit of debris. *Thyone's* body resembles a distorted football with a mouth at one end and an anus at the other. The mouth is surrounded by ten short, branching tentacles which retract when the animal is disturbed. The body is covered with short tube feet or podia more or less uniformly distributed over its surface. The podia on the bottom of the sea cucumber have suckers, those on top lack suckers. *Thyone* usually lives buried in the mud with both ends of its body extended to the surface. If uncovered, it may require several hours of slow burrowing to rebury itself. *Thyone* eats plankton which it entangles in mucous on its tentacles as they are waved through the water. When severely disturbed, *Thyone* may undergo a process known as evisceration, during which its anterior end and gut are discarded. The wound quickly heals and a new mouth, tentacles and gut are slowly regenerated. A sea cucumber may be stimulated to eviscerate if overcrowded or if kept in an aquarium without adequate circulation.

The virgin nerite, *Neritina virginea* (Figure 7.35), is one of the most colorful grass flat snails on the northwestern Gulf Coast. Its shell pattern and color are extremely variable. It may be white, gray, yellow, olive, red, purple, or black, and its pattern may consist of stripes, waves, large or small triangular dots or fine lines. Live *Neritina* may be found crawling over the mud surface or on the grass stalks at night or on cloudy days, but its shells are most conspicuous when inhabited by the more active hermit crabs. It is most common along the south Texas coast. It lays eggs during the winter in yellow gelatinous capsules on its own shell or that of another mollusk.

Figure 7.34. The sea cucumber, *Thyone mexicana*. (x 2.5)

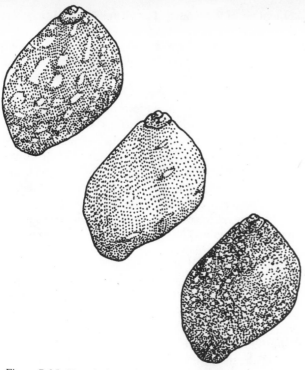

Figure 7.35. The virgin merite, *Neritina virginea*, with several shell patterns. (x 3)

The Carnivorous Whelks

Two species of large whelks, *Busycon perversum pulleyi:* and *Busycon spiratum* (Figure 7.36), are common in the bay, though their occurrence in shallow water may be seasonal. The former species is the more common one. They are easily distinguished by the direction of coiling of the shell. *Busycon perversum* has a "left-handed" shell and *Busycon spiratum* coils to the right, as do most snails. One may determine the "handedness" of a shell by trying to insert one hand and then the other with the thumb on the apex of the shell. The hand that curls naturally in the same direction as the shell is coiled indicates the handedness. The two species of *Busycon* can also be distinguished by the color of their flesh. *Busycon perversum* has a black body, and *Busycon spiratum* has a pale orange body with black tentacles. Both of these species feed on small bivalves such as *Ensis minor* and small *Mercenaria campechiensis*. The clams are grasped by the foot and may be forced open by wedging the edge of the lip between the clam's valves. Once the valves are opened, *Busycon* rasps the flesh away with its radula. The abundance of large whelk shells occupied by hermit crabs attests to the snail's longevity.

Both species lay their eggs in disklike capsules. *Busycon perversum* produces 50-175 capsules in a string (Figure 7.37) and lays up to 200 eggs in each capsule, and *Busycon spiratum* produces a smaller

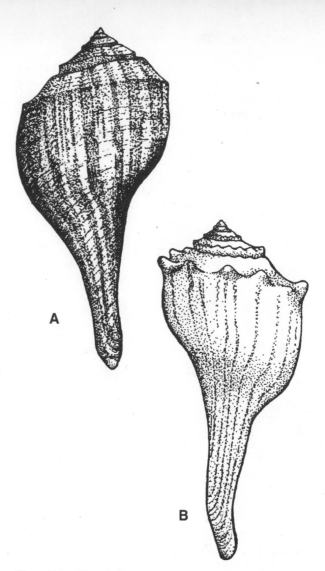

A

B

Figure 7.36. The whelks *Busycon spiratum* (A) (x 1) and *Busycon perversum pulleyi* (B). (x 0.8)

Figure 7.37. Egg capsules of *Busycon perversum pulleyi*. (x 1)

string with fewer eggs per capsule. The proximal end of the string is anchored in the sand, and the last few capsules added to the string are usually small and devoid of eggs. Strings of these sculptured capsules that become unmoored can occasionally be found washed up on the shore. The young pass through all of their larval stages within the capsule, emerging as miniature snails.

Figure 7.38. The Texas tusk shell, *Dentalium texasianum,* in a feeding position. (x 3)

Tusks and Bubbles

The Texas tusk shell, *Dentalium texasianum* (Figure 7.38), also lives in inlet influenced portions of our bays. It is easily recognized by its slender tapering, curved shell which is hexagonal in cross-section. *Dentalium* is not a snail, as might be suspected, but rather a member of the related class Scaphopoda. It burrows into the sediment by extending its muscular foot out of the large end of the shell as a digging tool. Only the tip of the small end of its shell is left protruding above the surface. A respiratory current is maintained through the hole in this exposed tip. When buried, *Dentalium* uses probing motions of its foot to pack the sediment away from the buried end of the shell, forming a feeding cavity. Knobbed tentaclelike structures called captacula arise from near the mouth and scour the surface of this cavity for bits of detritus which are collected and passed to the mouth. When this feeding cavity has been cleaned, *Dentalium* pushes itself up through the sediment and moves to a new site to begin the process again. The shells of Pacific Coast species of *Dentalium* were once used as currency by Indians.

The bubble shell, *Bulla striata* (Figure 7.39), is a small carnivorous opisthobranch that burrows in the mud flat. Its shell is very thin and has an aperture that extends along the entire length of the shell. *Bulla* completely envelops its shell in its mantle, much like *Polinices* and *Sinum*. It remains buried during the heat of the day; thus it is most readily found at night or on overcast days.

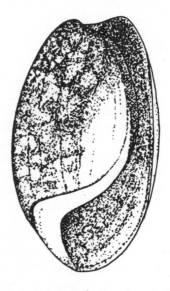

Figure 7.39. The bubble shell, *Bulla striata*. (x 4)

8

Artificial Reef Habitats

Since completion of the first successful oil well in the Gulf of Mexico in 1938, approximately 900 major platforms and thousands of support structures have been constructed in the Gulf. In an environment where such habitat is rare, each of these structures provides habitat for numerous organisms dependent on a hard substrate for attachment. A typical major platform in 20 meters of water may provide over one-half acre (0.2 ha) of hard substrate. The average existing platform is over 16 years old, and several are nearly 30 years old, offering ample time for the development of a rich community.

Such long time intervals are not required, however. Although the process may be delayed slightly by the use of antifouling paints, populations of bacteria and diatoms may reach densities of several thousand individuals per square centimeter within 24 hours after a new surface becomes available. This bacterial slime favors subsequent colonization of the new habitat by protistans, algae, barnacles, and numerous other organisms. Depending on the time of year and the proximity to other structures or shipping lanes, a thick coat of organisms may develop in less than a fortnight.

As might be expected, this biota is very similar to that which encrusts the hulls of ships, and thus many common species are cosmopolitan in distribution. These "fouling" organisms add a rough texture to the submarine surfaces of the structure, providing a maze of crevices in which crabs, shrimp, worms, and other motile animals can take refuge from wave forces and predatory fish. This is especially true of structures encrusted by the giant barnacle *Balanus tintinnabulum,* which often grows atop others of its species to form a honeycombed layer 10-15 centimeters thick.

Oil field structures are not the only artificial reef habitats in the Gulf of Mexico. Many sunken ships serve the same function. A dozen liberty ships have been sunk intentionally off the Texas coast in recent years in hope of attracting game fishes for recreational fishing and diving. Such reefs may last over 100 years before their ultimate destruction by marine corrosion.

Barnacles Upon Barnacles

Probably the most significant event in the colonization of an artificial reef by fouling organisms is the arrival of barnacles. Usually more numerous than oysters or mussels, their longevous shells greatly increase the size of the colonizable surface and the number of refuges for more cryptic cohabitants. The barnacle species most prevalent on oil platforms are the giant barnacle, *Balanus tintinnabulum* (Figure 8.1), and various members of the *Balanus amphitrite* complex of species. The latter group includes *Balanus*

Figure 8.1. Cluster of giant barnacles, *Balanus tintinnabulum*. (x 0.3)

reticulatum, which is common off Louisiana under the influence of Mississippi River runoff.

Balanus tintinnabulum is a cosmopolitan species often found encrusting ship hulls and, consequently, wharf pilings in ports around the world. They are also found on the rocky shores of western Africa and the eastern and western coasts of North America. It is primarily an intertidal species, and thus reaches its maximum abundance near the sea surface on Gulf of Mexico oil platforms. However, it is a dominant structural feature as deep as 10 meters below the surface, and scattered individuals may be found deeper than 20 meters. Its large shell is not only shared by dozens of species while the barnacle lives, but is inhabited by various crabs, shrimp, and fish after its death. One curious inhabitant is the crested blenny, *Hypleurochilus geminatus,* whose demonic appearance and aggressive antics have delighted many alert divers. One of these little fish seems to be nestled in each empty barnacle shell, poised to dart forth to challenge all trespassers or to graze algae, hydroids, and amphipods found on the shell surface.

Barnacles growing too near the sea surface or attached to other barnacles in unstable hummocks are often easily dislodged by storm waves or grazing fish. Even then they contribute to the development of the reef-associated biota. Snails and hermit crabs aggregate at the bases of platforms to consume the dislodged food. The empty shells continue to serve as shelter for mud crabs and young octopuses. Clusters of *B. tintinnabulum* shells are also prized as coffee table conversation pieces. The shell's color can be preserved by coating it with an artist's varnish. Cleaning the shell of unwanted sponge, algae, and hydroids is an arduous task that may be lightened with the aid of such garden pests as ants and pillbugs. A successful association with these scavengers requires soaking the shell in freshwater to leach as much salt as possible out of the unwanted tissues before placing the shell in a shaded part of the garden. Too much salt will preserve the tissue; too much sun will bleach the shell.

Balanus tintinnabulum is apparently a longevous barnacle that does not reproduce as readily as other barnacle species in the Gulf. Young individuals are rarely observed; small barnacles with reddish stripes, which may appear to be young *B. tintinnabulum,* frequently belong to the *Balanus amphitrite* complex of barnacle species. Like *B. tintinnabulum, B. amphitrite* is an extremely variable species with a world-wide distribution in temperate and tropical waters. Several of the *B. amphitrite* subspecies have been elevated in rank to species, now belonging to the *B. amphitrite* "complex."

Three of these species commonly found in the Gulf of Mexico are *B. amphitrite amphitrite, B. venustus*

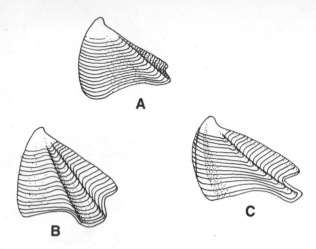

Figure 8.2. Tergal plates of *Balanus venustus* (A), *Balanus amphitrite* (B) and *Balanus reticulatus* (C). (x 15)

niveus, and *B. reticulatus* (Figure 8.2). *Balanus amphitrite amphitrite* is an intertidal species that apparently invaded the Gulf of Mexico during the first half of this century with the aid of foreign shipping. *Balanus venustus niveus* is a predominately subtidal species, which is apparently more common in the eastern Gulf than west of the Mississippi Delta. *Balanus reticulatus* is reported as common on oil structures off the Louisiana coast, but its distribution extends to Japan, where it fouls cultured oysters.

Add Soft Colors and Textures

Barnacles are often disguised by one or more layers of other organisms, among the most colorful of which are sponges. The abundance of sponges on artificial reefs, particularly those which reach the sea surface, such as oil platforms, is typically obscured by algae, hydroids, and bryozoans growing on their exposed surfaces.

Among our most common species are encrusting sponges of the genus *Haliclona,* which spread over the substrate in a mat ranging from a little over 1 millimeter to nearly 2 centimeters in thickness. Their growth form varies considerably. Some individuals have their oscula, or excurrent pores, raised on pinnacles resembling tiny volcanos, as is typical for *Haliclona loosanoffi* (Figure 8.3). Other individuals are so smooth that they are easily mistaken underwater for a coat of paint. Color is also variable. *Haliclona rubens* is characteristically brick red, and *H. viridis* is usually yellowish green. The color of *H. permollis* ranges from lavender to deep purple; that of *H. loosanoffi* is usually tan or cream, but may appear to be dingy gray because of the adhesion of other organisms and detritus. *Haliclona permollis* may also

Figure 8.3. Colony of the sponge *Haliclona loosanoffi* growing over a barnacle cluster. (x 0.5)

Figure 8.4. The calcareous sponge, *Scypha barbadensis*. (x 10)

be gray when growing in shade. This species inhabits the littoral zone (at 0.5 meter above MLLW) in Oregon.

Haliclona rubens and *H. viridis* are common in the West Indies, where they form massive and branching colonies in addition to the encrusting form familiar in the Gulf. *Haliclona permollis* and *H. loosanoffi* have more northern affinities, the latter species being found along the Atlantic coast to Connecticut, where it commonly inhabits eelgrass beds. Its planktonic larvae are negatively phototactic and thus typically settle on the under surface of submerged objects.

Yellow or beige colonies of *Halichondria bowerbanki* are often found among colonies of *Haliclona*. *Halichondria* colonies superficially resemble those of *Haliclona loosanoffi*, and cannot usually be distinguished without microscopic examination of the spicules. *Halichondria* spicules are 0.2-0.4 millimeters long, 2-3 times the size of *Haliclona loosanoffi* spicules. Adjacent colonies of *Halichondria* often fuse as they grow into one another. This species generally prefers habitats where strong currents are experienced.

The boring sponge, *Cliona celata*, is also found on oil platforms in the shells of oysters and barnacles. Perhaps the least conspicuous sponge found on artificial reefs is a small calcareous sponge, *Scypha barbadensis* (Figure 8.4). Seldom over 8 millimeters high and appearing like a tiny puff ball, this sponge is most easily observed when it colonizes portions of the substrate that have been denuded by the removal of a barnacle cluster or oyster. Its single osculum is ringed by long, slender spicules, and smaller spicules bristle from the body wall.

Its sponge fauna is severely limited by a variety of the northern Gulf's most prominent characteristics. Low winter temperatures discourage many species common in the Caribbean, southern Florida and Yucatan. Numerous rivers add millions of tons of

sediment that smothers sponges growing too near the bottom or on horizontal surfaces off the bottom. Rapid summer algal growth smothers sponges growing too near the sea surface. Thus, the northern Gulf's sponges thrive best on submerged reefs far from shore, where the water is clearer, or on the vertical surfaces of artificial reefs at intermediate depths. Unfortunately, such habitats are not uniformly distributed in our region and the planktonic larvae of sponges are short-lived, making it difficult for them to colonize the new habitats that do appear.

Sponges cannot be identified reliably on the basis of shape or color. Determination of the size and shape of the spicules and microscopic examination of the tissue is usually required. Spicules can be easily extracted by dissolving a piece of tissue in a solution of sodium hypochlorite (Clorox), leaving the spicules behind. Addition of a weak acid will demonstrate the nature of the spicules: calcareous spicules (as in *Scypha*) will dissolve; siliceous spicules (as in *Haliclona* and *Cliona*) will not. Some spicule shapes commonly found in Gulf of Mexico sponges are illustrated in Figure 8.5.

Figure 8.5. Sponge spicules (A-C) and gorgonian spicule (D). (x 50)

Figure 8.6. Anterior end of *Haplosyllis spongicola* with extended proboscis. (x 15)

Figure 8.7. Anterior end of *Trypanosyllis gemmipara*. (x 10)

Serpentine and Mossy Forms

Sponges provide not only a secondary substrate for other fouling species, but a refuge for several motile species. Among those refugees with the greatest fidelity are the polychaetes *Haplosyllis spongicola* and *Trypanosyllis gemmipara*. These are omnivorous worms that feed through an eversible proboscis. When extended, the proboscis is tipped with a circlet of ten knobs. The tentacles and cirri of these cosmopolitan species have a beaded appearance. *Haplosyllis spongicola* (Figure 8.6) is a small, pale yellowish-orange worm; *T. gemmipara* (Figure 8.7) is pale yellow with reddish-brown to purple cirri and matching thin bands on the anterior dorsal surface. The southern clamworm, *Neanthes succinea* (Figure 7.23), is another omnivorous resident of this sponge-barnacle habitat. During the breeding season and oc-

casionally for migration, adult *Neanthes* leave this habitat and swarm to the sea surface. Such swarming has been observed in midwinter in the northern Gulf.

Algae, hydroids, and bryozoans grow over the sponges, as well as over portions of the habitat not occupied by sponge. Among the most conspicuous of these are the bryozoans *Bugula neritina* and *B. rylandi* and the hydroid *Tubularia crocea,* which often grow in colonies several centimeters in diameter and 2-5 centimeters thick. As its name suggests, *T. crocea* (Figure 8.8) resembles a cluster of flowers on long stems, making it difficult to remember that they are actually animals. Upon closer examination, each "flower" is seen to consist of two rows of tentacles, between which are located numerous gonozooids. The inner row of tentacles surrounds the mouth. *Tubularia* is neither a good invader nor resistant to the invasions of other species. It relies on its tolerance of low temperature and its rapid growth rate to bloom briefly during the winter and early spring.

Bugula neritina (Figure 8.9) initially resembles a coarse, reddish-brown alga, but once identified, the confusion vanishes. Subtle differences—its rough texture, frequent branching, large size—catch the eye. Each colony consists of a succession of individual zooids attached to one another in a zig-zag pattern, as if in continual doubt as to which way to turn. Each zooid is encased in a chitinous box equipped with a long aperture through which the zooid can extend its tentacles to feed. *Bugula's* eggs are brooded in a spherical chamber known as an ovicell, which develops during the reproductive season. *Bugula neritina* can be found in harbors around the world. Its congener, *B. rylandi* (Figure 8.10), can be easily distinguished by its lack of significant color and its remarkable avicularia, which are lacking in *B. neritina*. Located approximately in the center of each zooid, these avicularia protect the colony from its encrusting and predatory neighbors. They function as small claws, pinching intruders that come within

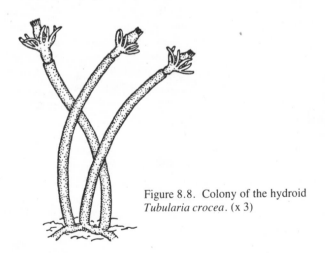

Figure 8.8. Colony of the hydroid *Tubularia crocea*. (x 3)

range. Each of these three species appears seasonally on Gulf of Mexico oil platforms. The bryozoans are more common during the summer, and *Tubularia* is most abundant during the winter months.

Several other bryozoans are common on artificial reefs. Of two common erect species, *Savignyella lafonti* (Figure 8.11) and *Aetea anguina,* the former is more easily seen due to its larger size and ornate branching structure. *Savignyella* is more brittle than *Bugula* and thus typically lives in sheltered areas. It can be found on exposed surfaces but does not attain its magnificently delicate and complex growth form unless protected from surge and current stresses. *Aetea* can be found by carefully examining bits of shell or sponge under a microscope. Unlike most other bryozoans, its zooids are not attached directly to one another, but are interconnected through a vine-like stolon. At first glance, the *Aetea* colony (Figure 8.12) often appears to be a tangled mass of stalks from

Figure 8.9. Colony of the bryozoan *Bugula neritina* (A) (x 1.5) with closeup of several zooids (B). (x 15)

Figure 8.11. Portion of *Savignyella lafonti* colony. (x 10)

Figure 8.10. Portion of *Bugula rylandi* colony. (x 15)

Figure 8.12. Portion of an *Aetea anguina* colony. (x 20)

which delicate hydranths or zooids have broken off. However, the right angle bend in these "stalks" provides the first clue to *Aetea's* identity. Closer examination reveals its scalloped orifice.

Encrusting bryozoans grow as a single layer of tightly packed zooids, each of which is attached to the substrate. Colonies on large, flat surfaces are typically circular, up to 6 centimeters in diameter, but they conform to the topographies of small, irregular surfaces. Species common in the northern Gulf of Mexico are *Schizoporella errata, Membranipora savartii, Membranipora tenuis,* and *Parasmittina trispinosa.*

As its specific name suggests, *Parasmittina* (Figure 8.13) is easily recognized by the three oral spines located just above its orifice. Numerous small pores can be seen around the periphery of the exposed upper surface of each zooid. Three small teeth, the center one largest and flattened, can usually be seen along the lower margin of the orifice. *Schizoporella* (Figure 8.14) has small pores, each sunk in a small pit, distributed rather uniformly over its upper surface. Like *Parasmittina,* each *Schizoporella* zooid may be protected by a single avicularium located near its orifice. Appearing somewhat like an ice cream cone, the tapered end of the avicularium is a hinged mandi-

Figure 8.15. Portion of a *Membranipora savartii* colony. (x 40)

Figure 8.16. Portion of a *Membranipora tenuis* colony. (x 40)

Figure 8.13. Portion of a *Parasmittina trispinosa* colony. (x 40)

Figure 8.14. Portion of a *Schizoporella errata* colony. (x 40)

ble, often with a terminal fang, which can snap shut on potential bryozoan predators. *Membranipora* has a quite variable aperture, which may extend over most of the zooid's exposed surface. This aperture is typically protected by jagged dentition around its lip, which is concentrated on a basal tooth in *M. savartii* (Figure 8.15) and more dispersed in *M. tenuis* (Figure 8.16). *Membranipora* lacks avicularia.

Several hydroids other than *Tubularia* are found on artificial reefs, the most common species being *Obelia dichotoma* (Figure 8.17) and *Clytia cylindrica.* Colonies generally appear as a whitish fuzz less than 1 centimeter high, but old *Obelia* colonies often develop a shrub-like structure several centimeters tall. *Clytia* colonies (Figure 8.18) typically have few branches, with most zooids arising directly from a common stolon. Its hydrothecae are at least twice as long as they are wide and have a serrate margin bearing 10-12 teeth. *Obelia's* hydrothecae are about 1.5 times as long as wide and have a smooth margin, which is often slightly flared. Its stems are often amber in color, particularly in older colonies.

The sea feather hydroid, *Plumularia diaphana* (Figure 8.19), is easily distinguished from *Obelia* and *Clytia* by the attachment of its hydrothecae directly to the upper surfaces of the branches rather than on annulated stalks. Interspersed among these sessile cups

Figure 8.17. Portion of an *Obelia dichotoma* colony. (x 10)

Figure 8.18. Two zooids of the hydroid *Clytia cylindrica*. (x 12)

Figure 8.19. Portion of a *Plumularia diaphana* colony. (x 8)

Figure 8.20. Portion of a *Syncoryne eximia* colony. (x 20)

packed with nematocysts. This is a primitive arrangement that has given way to the more familiar circelet of tentacles on most modern species. *Syncoryne's* hydranths arise from a stem which typically possesses numerous wrinkles or sloppy annulations.

Denizens of the Crevices

Among the motile animals associated with the sponge-barnacle complex are the brittle stars *Ophiactis savignyi* (Figure 8.21) and *Ophiothrix angulata* (Figure 8.22). *Ophiactis* is often very abundant on offshore oil platforms and on large sponges living on coral reefs such as the Flower Garden Bank off Texas. Juveniles typically have 6 or 7 arms, and adults typically have 5 arms. It is usually yellowish brown or yellowish green, with darker bands along the arms. *Ophiactis savignyi* is a cosmopolitan species inhabiting tropical and subtropical seas. Elsewhere in the world it is found in mangrove and rocky intertidal habitats. *Ophiothrix* is common in shallow water from North Carolina and Bermuda to Panama. It has 5 arms, and individuals from our area are maroon or reddish purple on the upper surface and paler underneath. A pair of maroon stripes extends along each arm. The glassy arm spines, which are slightly longer than the width of the arm, are equipped with rows of thorn-like teeth pointing outwards. Similar teeth are also found on the largest spines covering the central disk. Brittle stars are occasionally eaten by spadefish and filefish grazing on the fouling fauna of oil platforms.

Brittle stars share crevices with a variety of amphipods. The most commonly encountered species include *Jassa falcata, Erichthonius brasiliensis* and *Leucothoe spinicarpa*. Each of these species is widely distributed and quite variable in form. *Jassa* and *Erichthonius* are sexually dimorphic, the males being most easily recognized by claws with exaggerated

are club-like defensive structures called nematophores, which bear clusters of nematocysts. Like *Obelia,* its hydrothecae have a smooth margin. More intriguing yet is *Syncoryne eximia* (Figure 8.20), in which the hydranths are naked, lacking the protective hydrothecae. Moreover, the hydranths are covered with 20-30 tentacles, which are tipped with knobs

Figure 8.21. The brittle star *Ophiactis savignyi*. (x 6)

Figure 8.22. The brittle star *Ophiothrix angulata* (arms truncated) and a closeup view of an arm spine. (x 6)

Figure 8.23. The amphipod *Jassa falcata* (male). (x 15)

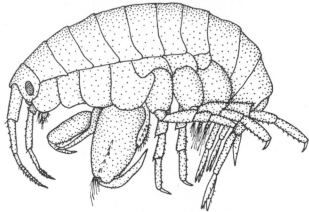

Figure 8.24. The amphipod *Leucothoe spinicarpa*. (x 15)

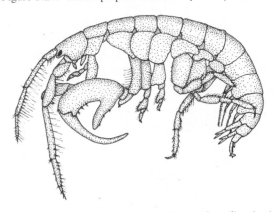

Figure 8.25. The amphipod *Erichthonius brasiliensis*. (x 15)

features. Amphipod claws are typically located on the second and third pairs of legs, and are usually subchelate, i.e. formed by folding the terminal leg segment back over the next segment to form a grasping appendage, such as is found on the praying mantis. In most amphipods the claws on the third legs are larger than those on the second legs. In male *Jassa* (Figure 8.23) the former claws are extremely large, and the next to the last segment has a spur-like "thumb" that extends out to meet the claw. *Jassa* is frequently darkly pigmented by an abundance of crimson spots.

Leucothoe (Figure 8.24) is also characterized by an oversized second claw, which is not restricted to the males, however. Its first, and smaller, claw is the more exotic, having its subterminal segment overlapped by both the terminal claw and a spur extending from the third most terminal segment (the carpus). *Leucothoe*

is the largest common amphipod on our offshore oil platforms and is pale in color.

Like the closely related *Corophium*, *Erichthonius* is a tube-building amphipod. Its tubes are typically attached to hydroids or filamentous algae. Male *Erichthonius* (Figure 8.25) have an elongated second claw, which superficially resembles the unusual first claw of *Leucothoe*: the carpus has a long spur that extends parallel to the subterminal segment. Its color is brownish to dull orange, distributed among numerous dots. *Erichthonius* has been found throughout the Atlantic coastline from Rio de Janeiro to Norway and in the North Pacific near San Francisco.

Pillbugs, Crabs, and Sea Spiders

Careful examination of algal masses just below the sea surface for amphipod tubes should reveal several other fascinating creatures. Among these are one of our most unlikely amphipods, the skeleton shrimp, *Caprella equilibra* (Figure 2.20), the squat isopod, *Dynamene perforata* (Figure 8.26), and the sea spider, *Tanystylum orbiculare* (Figure 8.27). *Dynamene* somewhat resembles its close relative, *Sphaeroma* (Figure 2.6), but possesses a pronounced cleft in its telson, which resembles a heart-shaped hole in some individuals. It lives around the bases of barnacles in shallow water, where it has access to the algae upon which it grazes.

Tanystylum is not actually a spider, but belongs to a related group of arthropods known as pycnogonids. Its understandable confusion with spiders, which do not inhabit the sea, arises from its 8 long, slender legs. A pycnogonid has 4 eyes mounted in a short pinnacle

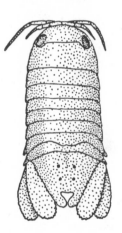

Figure 8.26. The squat isopod, *Dynamene perforata*. (x 10)

Figure 8.27. The sea spider *Tanystylum orbiculare*. (x 15)

Figure 8.28. The shore crab, *Pachygrapsus transversus*. (x 1.1)

on its back, giving it a remarkable 360-degree view of its world. *Tanystylum* ingests its food, consisting largely of hydroids, bryozoans, and sponges, through a proboscis and digests it in a gut whose branches extend nearly to the tip of each leg. Segments of food-packed gut can often be seen through the slender legs of this pale animal. Male sea spiders have an additional pair of legs, used to hold clusters of eggs which the male broods until they hatch.

A considerably larger resident of the littoral zone on oil platforms is the shore crab, *Pachygrapsus transversus* (Figure 8.28). Once a common resident of Texas jetties, this charming scavenger is now seldom seen nearshore. Even on oil platforms, its choice of habitat keeps it out of the view of most observers. It is restricted to the barnacle zone, where it can get a foothold against wave stresses, and it seldom ventures below the intertidal zone. Few divers or fishermen come close enough to the platforms at the waterline to espy this active crab.

Stone crabs, *Menippe mercenaria* (Figure 2.14), are abundant below the littoral zone. Juveniles (Figure 8.29) are particularly common on oil platforms and may be easily recognized by the arrays of chartreuse spots covering their dark brown carapaces. *Menippe* endures the company of several other crabs belonging to the family Xanthidae in this habitat. These crabs include *Panopeus turgidus*, *Pseudomedaeus agassizi*, *Hexapanopeus paulensis*, *Pilumnus dasypodus*, and *Pilumnus pannosus*.

The mud crab, *Panopeus turgidus*, is distinguishable from its congener in the bays, *Panopeus herbstii*, by its lack of a large blunt tooth near the base of the moveable finger of its large claw. *Hexapanopeus* (Figure 8.30) also has such a tooth, but is distinguishable from *Panopeus herbstii* by the presence

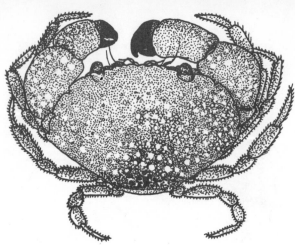

Figure 8.29. Juvenile stone crab, *Menippe mercenaria*. (x 1.2)

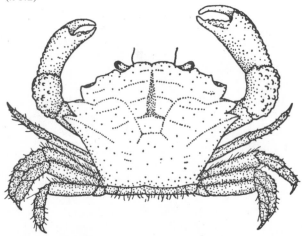

Figure 8.30. The mud crab *Hexapanopeus paulensis*. (x 3)

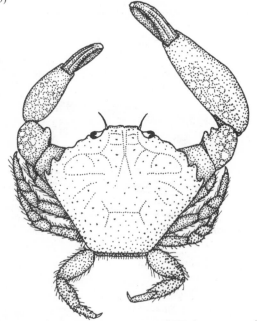

Figure 8.31. The mud crab *Pseudomedaeus agassizi*. (x 3)

of 10-15 granulated tubercles on the carpus ("elbow") of its large claw. On *Pseudomedaeus* (Figure 8.31) this coarse granulation is distributed over much of the carapace. These small mud crabs often take refuge within shells of deceased barnacles. Crabs that shun such precautions often fall prey to sheepshead and triggerfish.

The hairy mud crabs, *Pilumnus,* bear a pubescence over most of their bodies. The hair of *Pilumnus dasypodus* (Figure 8.32) is longer and less dense than that of *Pilumnus pannosus* (Figure 8.33). *Pilumnus* also has small spines on the upper surface of its claw and carpus, those on *Pilumnus dasypodus* being sharp and those on *Pilumnus pannosus* being blunt.

The arrow crab, *Stenorynchus seticornis* (Figure 8.34), crawls over the reef on extremely long, slender legs. Its long, jagged rostrum extends from a pear-shaped carapace, which is marked with black, brown and white stripes. The decorator crab, *Dromidia antillensis* (Figure 8.35), is less flashy. It further disguises its already drab carapace by carrying a sponge blanket on its back. This sponge is held in place by the

Figure 8.32. The hairy mud crab *Pilumnus dasypodus*. (x 2.5)

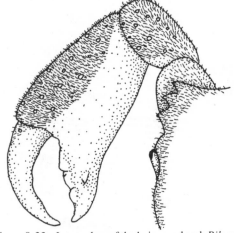

Figure 8.33. Large claw of the hairy mud crab *Pilumnus pannosus*. (x 5)

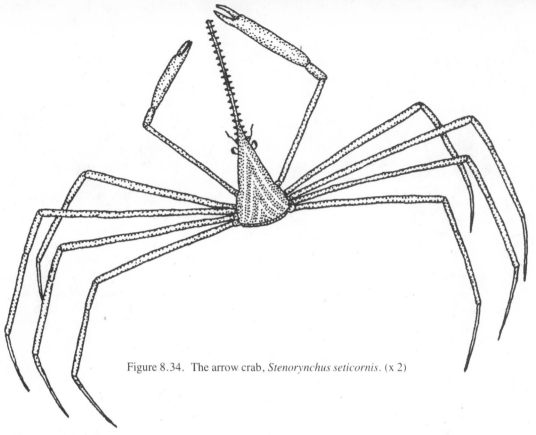

Figure 8.34. The arrow crab, *Stenorynchus seticornis*. (x 2)

crab's hindmost legs, which are raised over its carapace for this function. The sponge is contoured to the crab's back by a combination of sponge growth and pruning by the crab. A secondary coat of hydroids, algae, and bryozoans over the sponge usually completes the disguise.

The red crab, *Cronius ruber* (Figure 8.36), can often be found in or near large crevices on the reef. It is recognized as one of the swimming crabs by its paddle-like posterior legs. However, its maroon color is distinctive, as is the alternating pattern of large and small spines on the sides of its carapace.

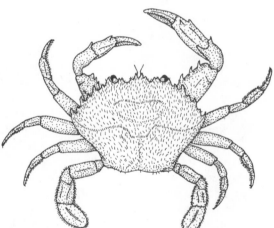

Figure 8.36. The red crab, *Cronius ruber*. (x 0.5)

Figure 8.35. The decorator crab, *Dromidia antillensis*, with its sponge overcoat. (x 4)

Among the most abundant crustaceans on offshore oil platforms is the snapping shrimp, *Synalpheus fritzmuelleri* (Figure 8.37). Unlike *Alpheus,* the snapping shrimp commonly encountered in the bays, *Synalpheus* lacks epipodites, which are outgrowths from the first segment of the walking legs. Mature *Synalpheus* have a reddish body and green claws, which become darker toward the tips of the fingers.

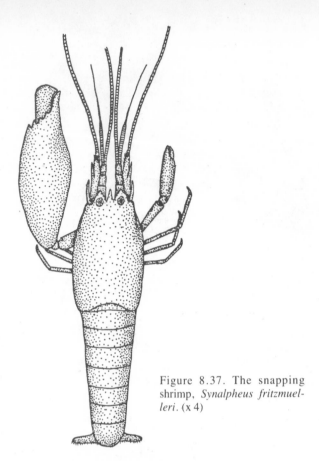

Figure 8.37. The snapping shrimp, *Synalpheus fritzmuelleri.* (x 4)

Clams, Oysters, and Mussels

Offshore oil platforms are inhabited by a variety of bivalves, some of which cement themselves directly to the substrate *(Ostrea equestris, Chama macerophylla),* some attach themselves via byssal threads *(Pteria colymbus, Brachidontes exustus, Isognomon bicolor),* and others bore into the shells of other bivalves and barnacles *(Lithophaga bisulcata, Lithophaga aristata).* The horse oyster, *Ostrea equestris* (Figure 8.38), is among the largest of these bivalves, and its heavy oval shell may reach 7-8 centimeters in diameter. Unfortunately, it is not sufficiently abundant to warrant commercial interest. The leafy jewel box, *Chama macerophylla* (Figure

Figure 8.38. The horse oyster, *Ostrea equestris.* (x 0.5)

8.39), is often more abundant, but too small to harvest. The surface of its upper shell is covered with scale-like plates, making it one of our most ornate bivalves. A thin coating of orange or red sponge often enhances its natural beauty.

The mossy ark, *Arca imbricata* (Figure 8.40), and the Atlantic wing oyster, *Pteria colymbus* (Figure 8.41), dwell within deep recesses formed by joints of the oil platforms. Clinging by byssal threads provides them flexibility and mobility to face environmental changes produced by wave stresses or encroachment by neighboring barnacles. Secreted within a groove in the bivalve's foot, byssal threads can be replaced or repositioned to enable an effective, although extremely slow, mode of locomotion. Both of these species are filter feeders. In sheltered areas they may survive to reach lengths up to 10 centimeters.

The pygmy venus clam, *Chione grus* (Figure 8.42), also attaches its shell within crevices on the reef. This tiny filter feeder is less than 1 centimeter long. Its shell is grayish white and often has a dark band along the posterior edge. This color is typically hidden by a layer of sponge or hydroids.

Hidden among hydroids and sponges, juvenile scorched mussels, *Brachidontes exustus* (Figure 8.43), also use byssal threads to attach themselves to barnacles or other bivalves. Somewhat more demanding in its choice of habitat, the two-toned tree oyster,

Figure 8.39. Shell of the leafy jewel box, *Chama macerophylla.* (x 8)

Figure 8.40. Shell of the mossy ark, *Arca imbricata.* (x 0.5)

Figure 8.41. Shell of the Atlantic wing oyster, *Pteria colymbus.* (x 0.7)

Figure 8.42. Shell of the pygmy venus clam, *Chione grus*. (x 12)

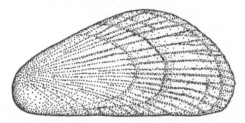

Figure 8.43. Shell of the scorched mussel, *Brachidontes exustus*. (x 10)

Figure 8.44. Shell of the two-toned tree oyster, *Isognomon bicolor*, with a view of its square teeth. (x 8)

Isognomon bicolor (Figure 8.44), usually resides within the shells of deceased barnacles or within narrow crevices between barnacles. However, it can often be found sharing the shells of living barnacles. The shape of its shell is extremely variable, but it usually appears quite flattened and fragile. Its valves converge on a relatively straight hinge bounded by a row of 4-8 square teeth. Both *Brachidontes* and *Isognomon* are filter feeders.

Clusters of large barnacles broken from the reef will often display short tunnels excavated in their bases by boring clams or mussels. Among the most common of

these borers are the mahogany date mussel, *Lithophaga bisulcata,* and the scissor date mussel, *Lithophaga aristata* (Figure 8.45). Both of these mussels are about 3 centimeters long, mahogany in color, and shaped like a torpedo or slender bread date. The scissor date mussel is easily distinguished by the crossed posterior tips of its shell, resembling exaggerated tips of a pair of scissors. These mussels also bore into rocks along the jetties, which is undoubtedly more difficult but more stable than boring barnacle shells.

The purple sea urchin, *Arbacia punctulata* (Figure 2.17), is a common predator of many fouling species. Its grazing on algae, hydroids, bryozoans, and various incidental species frees substrate for new colonists. Although its numerous tube feet adequately attach it to oil platform legs at moderate depths, it seldom finds shelter from wave stresses near the sea surface. Hence, the intertidal and shallow subtidal fauna usually enjoys freedom from urchin grazing. Juvenile long-spined urchins, *Diadema antillarium* (Figure 8.46), are occasionally seen on oil platforms. Unlike *Arbacia,* the long-spined urchin is a tropical species usually associated with coral reefs. Adult *Diadema* are deep purple, almost black, in color, although white individuals occur sporadically. Juveniles have purple and white banded spines, which are much longer and more slender than those of *Arbacia.*

Calcareous tubes of serpulid polychaetes are a common sight on barren substrate created by urchin or fish grazing or by physical damage to barnacles. These tubes belong predominately to the serpulid worm, *Eupomatus protulicola* (Figure 8.47), and the feather duster worm, *Spirobranchus giganteus* (Figure 8.48). *Eupomatus* tubes are typically less than 3 centimeters

Figure 8.45. Shells of the mahogany date mussel. *Lithophaga bisulcata* (A), and the scissor date mussel, *Lithophaga aristata* (B). (x 3)

Figure 8.46. A juvenile long-spined urchin, *Diadema antillarium*, hidden within a barnacle cluster. (x 0.6)

Figure 8.47. The serpulid worm. *Eupomatus protulicola*, within its calcareous tube. (x 5)

Figure 8.48. Anterior end of the feather duster worm, *Spirobranchus giganteus*, within its calcareous tube. (x 1.6)

long and much more abundant than the large tubes of *Spirobranchus*. Each of these worms is equipped with an operculum, which is used to plug the tube's aperture in time of stress. These opercula are armed with spines to discourage pursuit by potential predators. *Eupomatus* possesses a circelet of spines that curve outward from the center. *Spirobranchus* possesses a branching antler-like spine in the center of its operculum. The feather duster worm is well known as a decorative, but shy, inhabitant of coral heads. Its elaborate feeding structure, from which it derives its generic and common names, consists of three concentric rings of radioles borne on paired stalks. These radioles are usually colorfully banded, making them a favorite subject of underwater photographers. This feeding structure traps suspended food particles and directs them to the worm's mouth through a series of ciliated grooves.

Although changes in the biota fouling surfaces of offshore oil platforms occur frequently, predictable patterns of change are seldom found. Change is assured by the short life spans of most fouling species. With the possible exception of the barnacle *Balanus tintinnabulum*, fouling species rarely persist for as long as a year. Thus, substrate is frequently relinquished. Colonists generally arrive as planktonic larvae being carried past the structure. The composition of this larval assemblage varies greatly in both time and space. Once established, most colonists have mechanisms for resisting further colonization. Arriving larvae are either physically attacked or simply included in the diets of resident species. This is not always successful, as demonstrated by the multilayered community that develops in the northern Gulf of Mexico. However, it does contribute to the sudden blooms and disappearances of species commonly observed on oil platforms. Whereas this unpredictability often frustrates our attempts to understand the processes involved in the development of fouling communities, it greatly enhances the pleasure we derive from repeated visits to the same artificial reef.

Oyster Reefs

The common eastern oyster, *Crassostrea virginica,* is a sessile bivalve that attaches permanently to almost any firm substrate below mean tide level. It is actually a fouling organism, but its commercial importance spares it that title. It can be found on jetties, pilings, boats and shells of other mollusks. But it is its affinity for other oysters that makes it ecologically as well as commercially important.

The oyster's planktonic larvae prefer shell to rock, glass or other hard substrates, although many of them must settle for a second choice. As the young oysters (spat) grow, they cement their shells to those of their neighbors forming a cluster. If this cluster forms on a site where passing currents bring more oyster larvae and a steady supply of planktonic food, it will continue to develop into a reef. As the oysters die new larvae settle on their shells, eventually producing a structure that may be several feet thick and miles long. Oyster reefs are typically elongate structures usually perpendicular to the prevailing currents. Exceptions are found among small reefs or where currents are very strong or where the bottom topography has a dominant influence. Those oysters nearest the current, and thus nearest the incoming food, grow most rapidly and are encountered first by settling larvae. Thus the reef tends to spread along a leading edge perpendicular to the current.

Oyster reefs are ecologically important as oases of solid substrate in the midst of a vast muddy terrain that is otherwise unsuitable for the survival of many species, such as barnacles and anemones, that require a firm base of attachment. Consequently, the reef fauna is similar to the jetty fauna. Oysters are filter-feeders. Particles are strained from the water current as it passes through the gills. These particles are passed along ciliated grooves to the mouth, where they are sorted by a pair of palps. The desired food is ingested; the rejected particles are wrapped in mucous and discarded as a by-product called pseudofeces. The oyster shell is asymmetrical: the right valve is flatter than the left valve. The left valve not only provides a natural bowl for the raw oyster fancier, but also helps to keep the lip of the shell above the sediments. *Crassostrea* may change sex several times during its lifetime. This ability is a safeguard against the accidental formation of a cluster of only one sex.

Reef Inhabitants

Some oyster reef inhabitants compete with the oysters for food and attachment sites. Prominent among these competitors are the hooked mussel, *Ischadium recurvum;* a small anemone, *Aiptasiomorpha texaensis;* the acorn barnacle; the common Atlantic slipper shell, *Crepidula fornicata;* and the serpulid worm, *Hydroides dianthus* (Figure 9.1). The hooked mussel is common on low salinity reefs, where it attaches by byssal threads. It is a small bivalve (2-6 centimeters long) with pronounced ribs and a sharply hooked beak. The acorn barnacles, (*Balanus improvisus, Balanus eburneus* and *Balanus amphitrite amphitrite,* are common on the high salinity reefs. *Hydroides* secretes a calcareous tube on the surface of a mollusk shell. Only the head and its crown of filtering tentacles protrude from this tube. When disturbed *Hydroides* withdraws into the tube and plugs the opening with its operculum.

Oysters are molested by a number of organisms that attack their shells and thus much of the oyster's energy is consumed for repair of the damaged shell. These species include the blister worm, *Polydora websteri;* the boring sponges, *Cliona celata* and *Cliona truitti;* and the oyster piddock, *Diplothyra smythii.* When young *Polydora* settle on an oyster shell they begin to etch out a shallow groove which is slowly expanded into a deep pit, where the worm lives curled like a horseshoe. The space in the center of the pit is filled with mud and detritus that have been cemented together with mucous. This forms the mud blister

Figure 9.1. The oyster community: the common eastern oyster, *Crassostrea virginica;* the hooked mussel, *Brachidontes recurvus;* the anemone, *Aiptasiomorpha texaensis;* the stone crab, *Menippe mercenaria;* the barnacle, *Balanus eburneus;* and the serpulid worm, *Eupomatus dianthus.*

often seen on the insides of oyster shells. The worm can be detected in living oysters by the presence of its two long, slender tentacles that wave freely in the water.

The boring sponges, *Cliona* spp., also etch holes in oyster shells. These holes, which are small (less than 2.5 millimeters in diameter) but numerous, are usually part of an extensive network of tunnels beneath the shell's surface. This network may be expanded until the shell is completely destroyed. The sulfur sponge, *Cliona celata,* prefers habitats where the salinity is higher than 15‰ at least half of the time and higher than 10‰ at least three-fourths of the time. It produces relatively large holes (1.5 to 2.5 millimeters in diameter) from which bright yellow tufts of sponge extend. In addition to oysters, the sulfur sponge is also destructive to coral, gastropod shells, and calcareous rock. It is expecially destructive to limestone break-waters in England. *Cliona truitti* is more euryhaline than *Cliona celata,* and is able to withstand habitats where the salinity drops to 10‰ or less about half the time. It is characterized by smaller holes than those of *Cliona celata.* It also produces gemmules, which are clusters of sponge cells surrounded by a protective

shield that is resistant to drying and to extreme temperatures. These gemmules insure the propagation of the species. Gemmules are typical of freshwater sponges.

The oyster piddock (Figure 9.2) is a boring clam that both bores into the oyster's shell and competes with it for food. Its boring activities weaken the oyster's shell, and it may occasionally break through the shell, requiring the oyster to secrete additional layers of shell over the intruder.

Figure 9.2. The oyster piddock, *Diplothyra smythii.* (x 5)

Oyster Predators

Many of the animals inhabiting oyster reefs are oyster predators, such as the drill, *Thais haemastoma,* and the stone crab, *Menippe mercenaria. Thais* bores a hole through the oyster's shell, usually between the lips where it is weakest, and extends its flexible proboscis through the hole to remove the oyster's flesh. The proboscis may be as long as the snail's shell. It contains the radula, which rasps off bits of oyster tissue, and the mouth and esophagus, which ingest these bits and transport them back to the snail's stomach.

The stone crab has powerful claws with which it chips off successive small fragments of the oyster's shell until it gains entry to the meat. A large stone crab may simply crush the shell of a small oyster. Two other crabs that are common reef inhabitants may be destructive to small oysters. The blue crab, *Callinectes sapidus,* and the common mud crab, *Panopeus herbstii,* become large enough to chip small oyster shells. *Panopeus* eats barnacles *(Balanus eburneus)* as well as small oysters. The flat mud crab, *Eurypanopeus depressus,* attacks oyster spat, but it is too small (2 centimeters wide) to be considered a serious threat to larger oysters. Another mud crab found on the oyster reefs, *Rithropanopeus harrisii,* is also too small (1.5 centimeters wide) to prey on most oysters.

Among the least conspicuous oyster predators are the flatworms, *Stylochus ellipticus* and *Stylochus frontalis,* which are called "oyster leeches" by oystermen. These wafer-thin animals are able to slip between the open valves of an oyster. The oyster may be able to blow the intruder out by rapidly expelling water from its shell, but persistence usually pays off for the flatworm. If unable to force the flatworm from its shell, the oyster may try to isolate it by building a wall around it. Unfortunately, the oyster must often leave a breach in this wall if it is to avoid cementing its valves together. The successful flatworm extends its proboscis to ingest the oyster's tissues.

Stylochus has numerous eyes, some of which are located on the tentacles and many of which are distributed in a band along the margin of the dorsal surface. In *Stylochus ellipticus* (Figure 9.3) this marginal band of eyes is limited to the anterior third of its body; in *Stylochus frontalis* the band completely encircles the dorsal surface, although it is wider at the anterior end. *Stylochus ellipticus* grows to a maximum length of about 25 millimeters; a large *Stylochus frontalis* may be twice that long. The color of the former species is quite variable, ranging from yellow to brown to gray. *Stylochus ellipticus* preys on both oysters and barnacles while *Stylochus frontalis* eats primarily oysters.

Figure 9.3. The flatworm, *Stylochus ellipticus.* (x 3)

Oysters as Shelter

Two small snails, *Diastoma varium* (Figure 9.4) and *Odostomia impressa* (Figure 9.5), are commonly found crawling on the oysters. *Diastoma* is slightly larger and darker than *Odostomia* and has a siphonal notch in the outer lip which *Odostomia* lacks. *Odostomia* is an ectoparasite which sits on the lip of

Figure 9.4. *Bittium varium.* (x 8)

Figure 9.5. The parasitic snail, *Odostomia impressa.* (x 10)

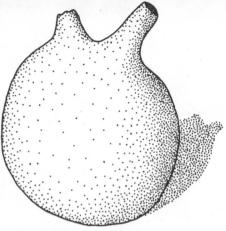

Figure 9.6. The sea squirt, *Molgula manhattensis*. (x 3)

Figure 9.7. The commensal crab, *Pinnotheres maculatus*. (x 3)

the oyster and extends its proboscis inside to feed on mucous and tissue fluids. *Diastoma* is apparently not harmful to the oysters. Similarly, the porcelain crab, *Petrolisthes armatus,* apparently uses the oyster reef primarily as shelter.

The sea squirt, *Molgula manhattensis,* (Figure 9.6), attaches itself to oysters, pilings, boat bottoms, submerged grass stalks and occasionally to hermit crab shells. It resembles a small (1-2 centimeters in diameter) gelatinous sphere with two short siphons attached to the upper surface. Seawater is drawn into the sea squirt through an inhalant siphon, passed through a fine mesh which removes the suspended food particles and forced out through an exhalant siphon. A stream of water may be expelled several centimeters into the air when the animal is exposed at low tide; hence the name "sea squirt." *Molgula* is usually pale green or olive, but it may be covered with

pieces of detritus or shell. This species is relatively tolerant of water pollution and is one of the few species of sea squirt that tolerates reduced salinities.

The oyster-au-naturel fancier may find a small soft crab nestled up against his delicacy. This is *Pinnotheres ostreum,* the oyster crab. These commensal crabs enter the oysters as larvae and become permanent residents. They usually live among the oyster's gills and steal food that the oyster has strained from the water. A related crab, *Pinnotheres maculatus* (Figure 9.7), is commensal with the pen shells, *Atrina* spp. Its carapace is covered with short brown hairs which are interrupted by a varied pattern of light spots. Though the carapace of *Pinnotheres ostreum* is similar in shape, it lacks the dense covering of hair. Both of these species are also found living commensally with other species of bivalves and with the worm *Chaetopterus variopedatus.*

Shell Habitats

Shells are a very common feature of shallow marine habitats. They provide support and protection from abusive surf, desiccation and predators. Organisms are more buoyant in seawater than in air, and hence require less skeletal support. However, intertidal species are periodically exposed to the air and thus need additional support. These species are also subjected to abrupt changes in pressure caused by waves passing overhead or shifting sand. Thus snails, barnacles, oysters, clams and hermit crabs make use of protective shells.

These shells also function as a substrate for dozens of small species that require a firm attachment. These species undoubtedly evolved from rocky shore species whose planktonic larvae found the shells an acceptable substitute for a rock, but most of them have become specialists in utilizing a shell substrate. Some of these species, particularly anemones and hydroids, offer the host some protection from potential predators in return for a place to live. Most of them, however, compete with their shelled hosts for food, impede the feeding or burrowing actions of the hosts or erode the shell so that it is more easily broken.

Shell inhabiting organisms appear to be most successful at invading shells utilized by hermit crabs. However, these shells are older than those still possessed by the original owner. Thus they have had a greater opportunity to encounter settling larvae of encrusting organisms. In addition, hermit crab shells are often found in habitats where other solid substrates are rare. A planktonic larva which has been carried by currents onto a mud flat rather than onto a jetty may have little choice of substrates. Traveling with a hermit crab has certain advantages: the shell is usually kept free of sediment and well aerated, and food is generally plentiful. But there are also disadvantages: the shell may be abandoned by the crab, or handled roughly or carried into unfavorable environments, such as up onto the beach.

Some invertebrates have defenses against settling larvae. Filter-feeding organisms, such as barnacles and oysters, simply include these larvae in their diets. Certain snails, such as the moon snail, *Polinices duplicatus,* and the lettered olive, *Oliva sayana,* extend the mantle over much of the exterior of their shells and then bury themselves in the sand, probably preventing the settling of larvae. Sea urchins, starfish and bryozoans have minute claws scattered over their surface which pick off larvae as they settle.

Shell Inhabitants

The most conspicuous inhabitants of shells along the northwestern Gulf Coast are the hermit crabs, *Clibanarius vittatus, Pagurus longicarpus, Pagurus pollicaris* and *Isocheles wurdemanni;* the barnacles, *Balanus improvisus* and *Balanus amphitrite amphitrite;* the white slipper shell, *Crepidula plana;* the encrusting bryozoan, *Membranipora commensale;* the amphipod, *Corophium louisianum;* the tanaid, *Leptochelia dubia;* the serpulid worm, *Hydroides dianthus;* young *Thais haemastoma;* the hydroids, *Hydractinia echinata* and *Podocoryne selena;* spat of the oyster, *Crassostrea virginica;* the boring sponges, *Cliona celata* and *Cliona truitti;* the boring polychaete, *Polydora websteri;* and the anemone, *Calliactis tricolor.*

Slipper Shells

Slipper shells can be found on most shells occupied by hermit crabs. Though not permanently attached to its host's shell, this snail stays in one place and its shell

Figure 10.1. The slipper shell, *Crepidula plana*, dorsal and ventral views. (x 1.5)

conforms to the shape of the host shell as it grows. They are filter-feeders, who lift their shells slightly to permit a current of plankton-laden water to flow underneath. Reproduction presents a problem for these sessile creatures, however, the males release their sperm into the water to seek out a mature female. Even with two slipper shells on the same host shell, the chances are 50-50 that they will be the same sex. However, *Crepidula* improves these odds through protandry, a sex reversal. All of these snails mature first as males, then become females. The male's metamorphosis into a female is retarded if there is another female nearby. The female broods the eggs under her shell until they hatch.

Crepidula plana (Figure 10.1) is a white slipper shell usually found inside shells occupied by hermit crabs. As it must often "arch its back" to fit snugly into the shell, it sometimes gives the appearance of being turned inside out. Its shell shape is as variable as the contour of its host. The common Atlantic slipper shell, *Crepidula fornicata*, can sometimes be found on the outer surface of lettered olive *(Oliva sayana)* shells. Its shell is light brown and much deeper than that of *Crepidula plana*.

Hydroids

Colonies of the hydroids, *Hydractinia echinata* and *Podocoryne selena* are occasionally found on shells occupied by either species of *Pagurus*. *Clibanarius* are rarely found inhabiting shells covered by these hydroids, as it appears to be more sensitive to the stings of the hydroids than is *Pagurus*. Thus the hydroids provide a refuge for *Pagurus* from the more abundant *Clibanarius*. The hydroid colonies look like white or pink fuzz covering the shell. Each hydroid colony is polymorphic, like those of *Physalia* and *Velella*, consisting of individual zooids that are specialized for different functions: support, defense, feeding and reproduction. These two hydroids can be distinguished by the nature of their skeletal spines: *Hydractinia's* are jagged and *Podocoryne's* are

smooth. All of the reproductive zooids in each colony are the same sex. Reproduction is probably aided by interactions among the hermit crabs. Spawning is synchronized to the daily light-dark cycle and usually occurs about one hour after dawn.

The larvae of *Balanus improvisus* and *Balanus amphitrite amphitrite* often find hermit crab shells a suitable spot to settle, and unfortunately for the crab, the latter species may also settle on its legs or eyestalks. It can also be found attached to other crustaceans, such as the rock shrimp, *Sicyonia dorsalis*. These barnacles grow very rapidly, probably a result of an abundant food supply. Adult barnacles can be found on crabs, indicating that they have grown to maturity since the crab's latest molt, because all of the barnacles on the crab's exoskeleton are shed with each molt. Since young crabs molt more frequently than older crabs, *Balanus amphitrite amphitrite* is more common on large, old crabs that have passed their terminal molt. This barnacle can usually be distinguished from *Balanus improvisus* by the purple marks on its shell.

The shells of dead barnacles and the deep umbilicus of *Polinices* shells are often inhabited by the amphipod, *Corophium louisianum*, or the tanaid, *Leptochelia dubia*. These minute crustaceans construct mud tubes in depressions. *Leptochelia* resembles an isopod, except that its second pair of legs have claws.

Bryozoans, Sponges, and Scaleworms

Another rapidly growing shell inhabitant is the encrusting bryozoan, *Membranipora commensale* (Figure 10.2). A colony the size of a quarter can develop within a month, forming a delicate mat on the surface of the shell. Each individual zooid is encased in a small coffinlike shell. Like most other shell inhabiting species, bryozoans are filter-feeders. They trap food particles in minute tentacles extended through the opening in the top of the shell. Their in-

Figure 10.2. Portion of a colony of the bryozoan *Membranipora commensale*. (x 30)

Figure 10.3. The boring sponge, *Cliona celata*, in an old *Busycon* shell. (x 1)

Figure 10.4. The serpulid worm, *Eupomatus dianthus*. (x 1)

Figure 10.5. The scaleworm, *Lepidonotus sublevis*. (x 1.6)

twelve pairs of large overlapping scales, or elytra, that cover its back. These scales are mounted on short pedicels, from which they readily break when handled. *Lepidonotus* probably lives on bits of food stolen from its host. This commensal worm is also found on sea pansies and starfish.

Anemones and Flatworms

Occasionally, especially during the winter months, a hermit crab will be found with an anemone on its shell. This anemone is usually *Calliactis tricolor* (Figure 10.6) although the warty sea anemone, *Bunodosoma cavernata,* will also attach to shells if a better substrate is unavailable. *Calliactis* can readily be distinguished from *Bunodosoma* because it lacks the hundreds of minute bumps that cover the surface of

tricate skeletons persist long after the host shell has dried out.

Occasionally a shell is found that is pierced by dozens of small holes, usually filled with yellow tufts when fresh. These holes were bored by the early growth stage of the sulfur sponge *Cliona celata* or its smaller relative *Cliona truitti* (Figure 10.3). These sponges chemically erode a network of tunnels within the shell, and their later stages completely dissolve the shell. The boring polychaete *Polydora websteri* also burrows into the shell, leaving a network of tunnels that weaken the shell. Unlike *Cliona, Polydora* may bore tunnels that are oblique to the surface of the shell so that several millimeters of the tunnel may be exposed. The serpulid worm, *Eupomatus dianthus* (Figure 10.4), also dwells in tunnels but it constructs its own calcareous tubes on the surface of the shell. The fanlike radioles of this worm may be extended from the tube if the shell is placed in a small dish of seawater and watched quietly for a short while.

The scaleworm, *Lepidonotus sublevis* (Figure 10.5), is a common inhabitant of hermit crab shells. Unlike *Polydora* and *Hydroides,* this polychaete does not construct a burrow but crawls about freely within the shell. When the hermit crab inhabits the shell of *Polinices duplicatus,* the scaleworm is often found in the shell's umbilicus. It is easily recognized by the

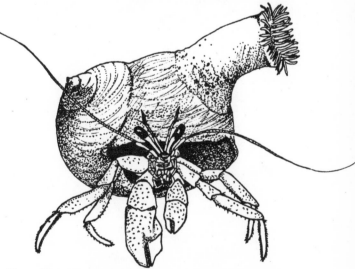

Figure 10.6. The anemone *Calliactis tricolor* attached to a *Polinices* shell inhabited by the hermit crab, *Pagurus pollicaris*. (x 1)

Bunodosoma. Like its hermit crab host, *Calliactis* has no lasting attachment for any particular shell and will readily abandon it if a more appealing surface comes along. Though this anemone is usually associated with hermit crabs of the family Paguridae, it is also found on the shells of live snails and on the carapaces of other crabs, such as the decorator crab *(Stenocianops furcata)* in Florida. *Calliactis* may also be found on other smooth surfaces, such as pieces of fiberglass or plastic, that are cast up on the beach.

Calliactis and its hermit crab host seem to cooperate to move the anemone onto the crab's shell. The crab may tap at the base of the anemone with its claws, causing the anemone to loosen its grip on its current substrate. Then the crab may pick the anemone up in its claw and hold it against its own shell until the anemone attaches.

The flatworm *Stylochus zebra* (Figure 10.7) is another species that can sometimes be found in *Pagurus* inhabited shells during the winter. It seems to

Figure 10.7. The flatworm, *Stylochus zebra.* (x 5)

prefer *Pagurus pollicaris* to *Pagurus longicarpus* as a host. This flatworm reaches a length of 3-4 centimeters and is flesh colored with conspicuous brown "zebra" stripes. It is apparently a cold loving species and is more common along the New England coast, where it may be found on pilings as well as in shells.

11

Plankton and Nekton

Plankton and Nekton

Nearly all of the marine invertebrates that have been discussed depend wholly or partially on plankton. Most planktonic organisms are microscopic but a few are surprisingly large. The one characteristic they all share is an inability to swim faster than one knot. Thus they are at the mercy of even moderate currents.

The planktonic fauna of the Texas bays is highly seasonal. Many of the species are sensitive to relatively minor changes in temperature, salinity, oxygen level or toxin in the water. The species composition may change markedly during a heavy rain or drought. Moreover, the larvae of most marine animals are planktonic, and these are usually seasonal in their appearance. Such organisms, which spend only a portion of their life cycles in the plankton, are collectively called meroplankton; those that are planktonic during their entire lives are called holoplankton. The most frequently encountered forms of holoplankton in the bays are copepods, medusae, ctenophores, chaetognaths, mysids and sergestid shrimp.

Perhaps the most common of our holoplanktonic species are the copepods of the genus *Acartia. Acartia tonsa* (Figure 11.1) is the best known of these copepods. It is a small, short-lived filter-feeder. During the summer, when the water is warmest, it completes its life cycle in less than two weeks. Its swimming motion is very jerky; it flits through the water propelled by its long antennules. It is a euryhaline species, i.e. it can tolerate a wide range of salinities. It is found in habitats ranging from the lower ends of the bayous to the hypersaline lagoons of the southern Texas coast.

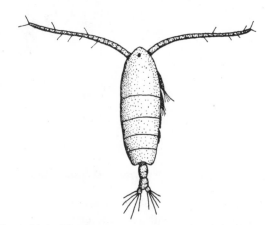

Figure 11.1. The copepod, *Acartia tonsa*. (x 40)

The chaetognath, *Sagitta tenuis* (Figure 11.2), is a copepod predator which is sporadically abundant. This chaetognath or "arrow-worm," as it is sometimes called, uses its long fins to glide through the water. Its large hooks flanking the mouth are used to capture copepods and other small crustaceans. Its size permits it to subdue even small fish larvae.

Among our most exotic animals are the sergestid shrimps *Lucifer faxoni,* (Figure 11.3) and *Acetes americanus louisianensis*. These small shrimps have their eyes mounted on long stalks—the ultimate in peripheral vision. Like many other plankters their presence is sporadic. *Acetes* is an estuarine species most abundant in low salinity bays. *Lucifer* is an oceanic species that moves into the bays during the summer. *Acetes* has minute claws on the last three pairs of legs on the first body section; *Lucifer* has only a rudimentary claw on the last pair of these legs.

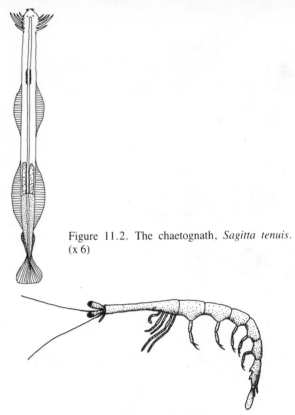

Figure 11.2. The chaetognath, *Sagitta tenuis.* (x 6)

Figure 11.3. The sergestid shrimp, *Lucifer faxoni.* (x 4)

Sea Nettles, Sea Wasps, and Sea Walnuts

Medusae or typical "jellyfish" are usually shaped like a bell or saucer, with tentacles and/or oral arms trailing behind them. They propel themselves through the water with pulsating contractions of the bell, which function much like the kick of a swimmer doing the breaststroke. The slender tentacles usually extend from the rim of the bell. The oral arms, which are typically longer and broader than the tentacles, are attached near the mouth under the bell. Both the oral arms and the tentacles, contain nematocysts, with which the medusa immobilizes its prey. The margin of the bell is the site of the compound sensory structures, the rhopalia, that control the orientation and beat of the medusa. These structures are spaced in multiples of four at regular intervals around the bell. The medusa is only one stage in the life of these animals; in many species it alternates with a sessile stage called a polyp, which resembles a small sea anemone. The polyp, which is called a scyphistoma, produces larvae through a budding process called strobilization. These larvae, the ephyrae, develop into the medusae. Each medusa produces either sperm or eggs and sheds them

into the seawater. After fertilization in the water, the zygote develops into another larva called a planula, which settles to the bottom and develops into a polyp. Thus the cycle is completed.

The most conspicuous medusa in our coastal waters is the cabbagehead, *Stomolophus meleagris* (Figure 11.4). This large oceanic medusa comes into the bays during the summer and frequently washes ashore in large numbers. These carcasses provide food for numerous shore dwellers, such as the stone crab, *Menippe mercenaria,* and the ghost crab, *Ocypode quadrata. Stomolophus* is a harmless filter-feeder, whose nematocysts are too weak to endanger man. It eats primarily copepods and the larvae of crabs and shrimp. Other animals, such as the spider crab, *Libinia dubia,* and the harvestfish, *Peprilus alepidotus,* hitch a ride or gain sanctuary in the bell. *Stomolophus* is easily recognized by its lack of tentacles and its short oral arms that are fused into a tight bundle.

Another jellyfish, somewhat less common that the cabbagehead, is the moon jellyfish, *Aurelia aurita* (Figure 11.5). This medusa is also a plankton feeder. Although it may have a diameter that exceeds that of *Stomolophus,* it is much less bulky. *Aurelia* can be recognized by its shallow bell fringed with numerous

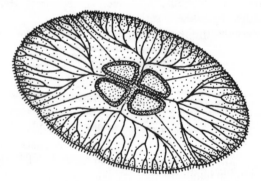

Figure 11.4. The cabbagehead medusa, *Stomolophus meleagris.* (x 0.3)

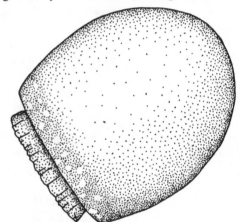

Figure 11.5. The moon jellyfish, *Aurelia aurita.* (x 0.3)

very short tentacles and its four short, unfused oral arms. The four lobes of its stomach are often visible through the bell. Small spider crabs are sometimes found on *Aurelia* and may burrow into the bell and feed on the tissues. These crabs probably crawl onto the bell when *Aurelia* brushes against the bottom or against submerged vegetation. Very large swarms of *Aurelia* are often observed offshore in midsummer or late autumn.

The sea nettle, *Chrysaora quinquecirrha* (Figure 11.6), occurs sporadically in our coastal waters. Its bell is about the same size as that of *Aurelia,* but it has fewer (24-40) and longer tentacles and longer oral arms. It is usually pale yellow or pink and sometimes has radiating stripes on the bell. *Chrysaora* spends the summer and early fall as a medusa and the winter and spring as a polyp. The colorless or pale pink polyps are often found attached to the undersides of oyster shells. The young medusae are produced in late spring or early summer and grow rapidly on a diet that consists primarily of the ctenophore, *Mnemiopsis mccradyi.* They in turn are eaten by adult spadefish, *Chaetodipterus faber.* As is the case with other medusae, *Chrysaora* is often found with spider crabs or young blue crabs riding on its bell. As its name suggests, the sea nettle's nematocysts can deliver painful stings, thus contact with this medusa should be avoided. Sea nettle stings are commonly experienced by divers taking advantage of warm summer temperatures by diving without wetsuits near offshore oil platforms. Individual reactions vary, but the pain generally persists as an irritating itching sensation for 15 minutes to several hours. The pain from nematocyst stings can often be relieved by applying meat tenderizer to the moistened wound.

The sea wasp, *Chiropsalmus quadrumanus* (Figure 11.7), is another medusa with a painful sting. *Chiropsalmus* prefers water with a high salinity; hence it is not common in northwestern Gulf Coast bays. However, during periods of prolonged drought, it may be found in large numbers. It prefers to stay near the bottom, and so is most often observed in shrimp trawls. Its diet seems to consist mainly of sergestid shrimp, shrimp larvae and crab larvae. *Chiropsalmus* is a cubomedusa, suggesting that the bell is somewhat cube shaped. It has four clusters of filamentous tentacles, each of which is attached to a single base located at one of the corners of the bell.

The lion's mane jellyfish, *Cyanea capillata versicolor* (Figure 11.8), is occasionally encountered during the winter months. This species is about the same size as *Aurelia* in the Gulf of Mexico, but may reach a diameter of over 2 meters in the Arctic. It has eight clusters of tentacles attached to the underside of the bell. The number of tentacles in each cluster increases

Figure 11.6. The sea nettle, *Chrysaora quinquecirrha.* (x 0.3)

as the medusa grows older. Like the sea nettle, *Cyanea* eats primarily ctenophores. The gulf butterfish, *Peprilus burti,* has been observed eating *Cyanea.*

The hydromedusa, *Nemopsis bachei* (Figure 11.9), is a small transparent jellyfish often abundant in the bays in winter and spring. It is only about 1 centimeter in diameter and thus easily overlooked. *Nemopsis* is more bell-shaped than most local common medusae, except perhaps the cabbagehead, *Stomolophus.* Its four radial canals are clearly visible, extending from

Figure 11.7. The sea wasp, *Chiropsalmus quadrumanus.* (x 0.5)

Figure 11.8. The lion's mane jellyfish, *Cyanea capillata versi-color*. (x 0.3)

Figure 11.9. The hydromedusa, *Nemopsis bachei*. (x 5)

its central digestive cavity to clusters of 16-18 tentacles on the edge of the bell. A cluster of oral tentacles can be seen inside the bell suspended from the junction of the radial canals. The radial canals usually seem swollen near their junction due to the gonads which extend about two-thirds of the length of these canals. The larvae produced by these medusae develop into sessile hydroids which in turn produce the next generation of medusae.

Ctenophores are similar to the medusae in that they are jellylike in appearance and are plankton feeders. They differ in that they lack the nematocysts that characterize the medusae. They are seasonal in their abundance, being most common in summer in the low salinity bays. They may be very abundant at one end of a bay and almost absent at the other end. The most common species on the northwestern Gulf Coast is the phosphorus jelly, *Mnemiopsis mccradyi* (Figure 11.10). It is a fairly large animal but is often overlooked because of its transparency. It is easily recognized by the two lobes that make up most of its

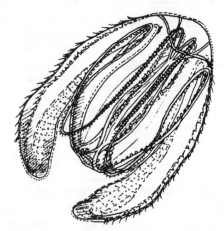

Figure 11.10. The phosphorus jelly, *Mnemiopsis mccradyi.* (x 1)

Figure 11.11. The sea walnut, *Beroë ovata*. (x 1)

Figure 11.12. The mysid shrimp, *Mysidopsis almyra*. (x 6)

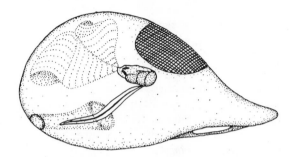

Figure 11.13. The larvacean, *Oikopleura sp.*, in its gelatinous house. Note the filtering screens, the food-gathering net and the escape hatch in the bottom of the house. (x 15)

bulk. Between these lobes are two retractable tentacles used in capturing prey. Like other ctenophores, *Mnemiopsis* has eight rows of cilia used to propel it through the water. Hence it is a very slow swimmer. The cilia are coordinated by an aboral sense organ that responds primarily to gravity. *Mnemiopsis* is a voracious predator on zooplankton: a single ctenophore may eat as many as 500 *Acartia* per hour. Unfortunately, *Mnemiopsis* also eats shrimp, crab and oyster larvae, and on several occasions it has been accused of seriously reducing the crop of oyster larvae. It is not, however, without voracious enemies of its own, including the medusae, *Chrysaora* and *Cyanea*, and the gulf butterfish.

Another ctenophore that can often be found in the bays is the sea walnut, *Beroë ovata* (Figure 11.11). It is about the same size as *Mnemiopsis* but is somewhat more flattened and lacks lobes and tentacles.

Ctenophores are luminescent organisms; light is produced in the walls of canals under the rows of cilia. Thus they seem to glow faintly in the dark, especially if disturbed. *Beroë* is usually the more common ctenophore during the winter, and *Mnemiopsis* is the more common species during the summer.

Mysids are small shrimplike crustaceans that swim just above the bottom in the bays and along the sandy beaches. *Mysidopsis almyra* (Figure 11.12) is one of the more common species of this area. Unlike the true shrimps, it has a beadlike equilibrium organ called a statocyst on each side of the tail fan, and its abdominal appendages or pleopods are much reduced. It uses its legs to stir up the water and to filter out any small plants, animals or detritus that pass by.

The larvacean *Oikopleura* spp. is certainly one of the most interesting planktonic organisms (Figure 11.13). It is quite small (3-4 millimeters long) but unmistakable in form. Its body consists of a kidney-shaped head which is perpendicularly attached to a long tail. Even more remarkable than the animal itself is the "house" that it constructs as a feeding aid. This house is equipped with two screens, which admit only very small food particles, and a finer mesh inside which collects these particles. The beating of *Oikopleura's* tail forces water through the house, at which time the food is removed. Eventually the screens become clogged with particles too large to pass through, and the house is abandoned and a new one is built. Nearly all species of *Oikopleura* are protandric, maturing as males first and then as females. Larvaceans resemble the larvae of sea squirts, to which they are related, hence the name "larvacean." The different species of *Oikopleura* are not easily distinguishable without the aid of a high resolution microscope.

Nekton

A few invertebrates that live in our bay waters are able to swim faster than one knot. Therefore, they cannot be considered plankton. These animals are included with the fishes as nekton. Our most conspicuous nektonic invertebrates are the squids. Two species are commonly found here: *Loligo pealei* (Figure 11.14) and *Lolliguncula brevis*. The latter species is smaller, reaching a maximum length of 23 centimeters and has rounded fins. *Loligo pealei* is longer, to one meter, more slender, and has triangular

Figure 11.14. The squid, *Loligo pealei*. (x 1)

fins. *Lolliguncula* is readily distinguished by its relatively large fins, which are 70-80% as wide as the mantle is long, compared to those of *Loligo,* which are only 45-55% as wide as the mantle length. *Loligo* is usually an offshore species, whereas *Lolliguncula* is more common in the bays. Both squids are widely distributed along the Atlantic coast of North and South America: *Loligo* is found from Nova Scotia to Venezuela and *Lolliguncula* from Chesapeake Bay to Brazil.

Squids have highly developed vision, which they put to good use in locating their prey. Locomotion is accomplished by a form of "jet" propulsion. A large water-filled cavity inside the squid is connected to the outside through a stubby siphon located under the squid's head. As the water is squeezed out of the cavity through the narrow opening in the siphon, it produces a rapid jet of water that pushes the squid in the opposite direction. Because the cavity must be refilled periodically the squid usually moves in short spurts. In contrast to the octopus, which has eight arms, squids have ten arms which they use for the capture of small fish and crustaceans. Two of the arms of the male squid are modified as copulatory structures. They pass small packets of sperm, the spermatophores, to the female and implant them in her mantel cavity. The squid's body is covered with chromatophores containing melanin which enable the squid to change its color. This pigment can also be secreted into the water from the "ink" gland, concealing the squid's retreat.

Appendix 1

A Note on Biological Terminology

All recognized species of organisms have a two-part scientific name. The first part is the name of the genus to which the species belongs, and it is always capitalized. The second part is the name of the species and is not capitalized. Although two species may have the same genus name *or* the same species name, no two species have both names in common. Species names are selected by the first person to publish a description of the organism, and they often refer to some physical property of the species (e.g. *Crepidula plana, Stylochus zebra, Chthamalus fragilis*), to the species' habitat (e.g. *Anemonia sargassensis, Glaucus atlanticus, Corophium louisianum*) or to some individual who is being honored (e.g. *Polydora websteri, Albunea gibbesii, Panopeus herbstii*). In formal usage the name of the person who described the species and the date that the description is published follow the species name, e.g. *Littorina irrorata* Say, 1822. If the species is later moved to a different genus, the describer's name is enclosed in parentheses, e.g. *Odostomia impressa* (Say, 1822). Frequently, one will see a species name followed by *L.* or *Linn.* These abbreviations refer to Linnaeus, an 18th century Swedish botanist who instigated the binomial nomenclature system and organized the known plant and animal kingdoms in his book *Systema Naturae*.

Most of the more conspicuous species have common names (e.g. blue crab, white shrimp) as well as scientific names. Unfortunately, these common names are of local origin, and a wide-ranging species may have several such names in various portions of its range. For example, *Sesarma cinereum* is known as the marsh crab, the wharf crab, the friendly crab and the square-backed crab in different parts of the world. Hence, common names are most useful in a local context and may not be helpful in communicating an organism's identity to someone living on a distant shore. One notable exception is the bird fauna for which one set of common names has become standard, at least among English speaking peoples, through extensive communication and common use of one set of guidebooks.

Abbreviations are commonly used when referring to organisms by their scientific names. When a name is used repeatedly or when two or more species in the same genus are mentioned, the first letter of the genus name may be used as an abbreviation after the first reference, e.g. *Balanus eburneus* and *B. improvisus*. Sometimes an organism is found whose genus is known, but that has not been identified further. Then the genus name is given, followed by the abbreviation sp., e.g. *Balanus* sp. If two or more species in the same genus are involved, this notation becomes *Balanus* spp.

Animal families, which are groups of related genera, have names that end in the suffix *-idae*. If no other common name exists, an abbreviation of the family name, formed by dropping the *-ae,* may be used. For example, a crab in the family Portunidae may be called a portunid crab.

Appendix 2

Phylogenetic List

Phylum Porifera
  Class Calcispongia
    Family Heterocoelidae
      Scypha barbadensis (Schuffner, 1877)
  Class Demospongiae
    Family Haliclonidae
      Haliclona loosanoffi Hartman, 1958
      Haliclona permollis (Bowerbank, 1866)
      Haliclona rubens (Pallas, 1766)
      Haliclona viridis (Duchassaing &
        Michelotti, 1864)
    Family Halichondriidae
      Halichondria bowerbanki Burton, 1930
    Family Clionidae
      Cliona celata Grant, 1826
      Cliona truitti Old, 1941

Phylum Cnidaria
  Class Hydrozoa
    Order Siphonophora
      Family Physaliidae
        Physalia physalis (Linnaeus, 1758)
    Order Chondrophora
      Family Velellidae
        Velella velella (Linnaeus, 1758)
      Family Porpitidae
        Porpita porpita (Linnaeus, 1758)
    Order Athecata
      Family Tubulariidae
        Tubularia crocea (Agassiz, 1862)
      Family Corynidae
        Syncoryne eximia (Allman, 1859)
      Family Hydractinidae
        Hydractinia echinata Fleming, 1828
        Podocoryne selena Mills, 1976
      Family Bougainvillidae
        Bougainvillia inaequalis Fraser, 1944
        Nemopsis bachei Agassiz, 1849

    Order Thecata
      Family Campanularidae
        Clytia cylindrica L. Agassiz, 1862
        Gonothyraea gracilis (Sars, 1851)
        Obelia dichotoma (Linnaeus, 1758)
      Family Plumularidae
        Aglaophenia late-carinata Allman, 1877
        Plumularia diaphana (Heller, 1868)
  Class Scyphozoa
    Order Semaeostomeae
      Family Ulmaridae
        Aurelia aurita (Linnaeus, 1758)
      Family Pelagidae
        Chrysaora quinquecirrha (Desor, 1848)
      Family Cyanidae
        Cyanea capillata (Linnaeus, 1758)
    Order Rhizostomeae
      Family Stomolophidae
        Stomolophus meleagris Agassiz, 1862
    Order Cubomedusae
      Family Chirodropidae
        Chiropsalmus quadrumanus (Muller, 1859)
  Class Anthozoa
    Order Gorgonacea
      Family Gorgoniidae
        Leptogorgia setacea (Pallas, 1766)
        Leptogorgia virgulata (Lamarck, 1815)
    Order Pennatulacea
      Family Renillidae
        Renilla mülleri Kölliker, 1872
    Order Actiniaria
      Family Actinidae
        Anemonia sargassensis Hargitt, 1908
        Bunodosoma cavernata (Bosc, 1802)
        Bunodactis texaensis Carlgren & Hedgpeth,
         1952
      Family Actinostolidae
        Paranthus rapiformis (Lesueur, 1817)

Family Hormathiidae
   Calliactis tricolor (Lesueur, 1817)
Family Aiptasiomorphidae
   Aiptasiomorpha texaensis Carlgren &
     Hedgpeth, 1952
Order Madreporaria
  Family Astrangidae
   Astrangia astreiformis Milne-Edwards &
     Haime,1849
Phylum Ctenophora
  Class Tentaculata
   Order Lobata
    Family Mnemiidae
     Mnemiopsis mccradyi Mayer, 1900
  Class Nuda
   Order Beroida
    Family Beroidae
     Beroe ovata Chamisso & Eysenhardt, 1821
Phylum Platyhelminthes
  Class Turbellaria
   Order Polycladida
    Family Stylochidae
     Stylochus ellipticus (Girard, 1850)
     Stylochus frontalis Verrill, 1893
     Stylochus zebra (Verrill, 1882)
    Family Planoceridae
     Gnesioceros sargassicola (Graff, 1892)
Phylum Rhynchocoela
  Class Anopla
   Order Heteronemertea
    Family Lineidae
     Cerebratulus lacteus Verrill, 1892
     Micrura leidyi (Verrill, 1892)
Phylum Annelida
  Class Polychaeta
   Order Phyllodocida
    Family Phyllodocidae
     Eteone heteropoda Hartman, 1951
     Phyllodoce mucosa Oersted, 1843
    Family Polynoidae
     Harmothoë aculeata Andrews, 1891
     Lepidonotus sublevis Verrill, 1873
    Family Glyceridae
     Glycera americana Leidy, 1855
    Family Nephtyidae
     Aglaophamus verrilli McIntosh, 1885
    Family Syllidae
     Haplosyllis spongicola (Grube, 1855)
     Trypanosyllis gemmipara Johnson, 1901
    Family Nereidae
     Ceratonereis irritabilis (Webster, 1879)
     Laeonereis culveri (Webster, 1879)
     Neanthes succinea (Frey & Leuckart, 1847)
     Platynereis dumerilii (Andouin & Milne-
      Edwards, 1833)

Order Capitellida
  Family Capitellidae
   Capitella capitata floridana Hartman, 1959
   Mediomastus californiensis Hartman, 1944
  Family Arenicolidae
   Arenicola cristata Stimpson, 1856
  Family Maldanidae
   Clymenella torquata (Leidy, 1855)
   Clymenella zonalis (Verrill, 1874)
Order Spionida
  Family Spionidae
   Paraprionospio pinnata (Ehlers, 1901)
   Polydora ligni Webster, 1879
   Polydora websteri Hartman, 1943
   Spiophanes bombyx (Claparéde, 1870)
  Family Paraonidae
   Aricidea fragilis Webster, 1879
  Family Chaetopteridae
   Chaetopterus variopedatus (Renier,1804)
   Spiochaetopterus costarum
Order Eunicida
  Family Onuphidae
   Diopatra cuprea (Bosc, 1802)
   Onuphis eremita oculata Hartman, 1951
  Family Lumbrinereidae
   Lumbrineris tenuis (Verrill, 1873)
Order Magelonida
  Family Magelonidae
   Magelona phyllisae Jones, 1963
Order Ariciida
  Family Orbiniidae
   Scoloplos capensis Day, 1963
   Scoloplos rubra (Webster, 1879)
Order Oweniida
  Family Oweniidae
   Owenia fusiformis delle Chiaje, 1841
Order Sabellida
  Family Sabellidae
   Hypsicomus elegans (Webster, 1884)
  Family Serpulidae
   Eupomatus protulicola (Benedict, 1887)
   Hydroides dianthus Verrill, 1873
   Spirobranchus giganteus (Pallas, 1766)
Phylum Mollusca
  Class Gastropoda
   Order Rhipidoglossa
    Family Neritidae
     Nerita fulgurans Gmelin, 1791
     Neritina virginea (Linnaeus, 1758)
   Order Ctenobranchia
    Family Littorinidae
     Littorina irrorata Say, 1822
     Littorina lineolata d'Orbigny, 1842
    Family Potamididae
     Cerithidea pliculosa (Menke, 1829)

Family Cerithiidae
Diastoma varium (Pfeiffer, 1840)
Family Epitoniidae
Epitonium tollini Bartsch, 1938
Family Janthinidae
Janthina janthina Linnaeus, 1758
Janthina pallida (Thompson, 1841)
Janthina prolongata Blainville, 1822
Family Calyptracidae
Crepidula fornicata (Linnaeus, 1767)
Crepidula plana Say, 1822
Family Ovulidae
Simnialena uniplicata (Sowerby, 1848)
Family Naticidae
Natica canrena (Linnaeus, 1758)
Poliniees duplicatus Say, 1822
Sinum perspectivum Say, 1831
Tectonatica pusilla (Say, 1822)
Family Cassididae
Phalium granulatum (Born, 1780)
Family Cymatiidae
Distorsio clathrata (Lamarck, 1816)
Family Terebridae
Hastula salleana Deshayes, 1859
Terebra dislocata Say, 1822
Terebra protexta (Conrad, 1846)
Family Buccinidae
Cantharus cancellarius (Conrad, 1846)
Pisania tincta (Conrad, 1846)
Family Nassariidae
Nassarius acutus (Say, 1822)
Nassarius vibex (Say, 1822)
Family Fasciolariidae
Fasciolaria lilium von Waldheim, 1807
Pleuroploca gigantea (Kiener, 1840)
Family Melongenidae
Busycon perversum pulleyi Hollister, 1958
Busycon spiratum plagosum (Conrad, 1863)
Family Columbellidae
Anachis semiplicata Stearns, 1873
Family Muricidae
Murex fulvescens Sowerby, 1834
Thais haemastoma canaliculata (Gray, 1839)
Thais haemastoma floridana (Conrad, 1837)
Family Olividae
Oliva sayana Ravenel, 1834
Olivella minuta (Link, 1807)
Order Dendronotoidea
Family Scyllaeidae
Scyllaea pelagica Linnaeus, 1758
Order Eolidoidea
Family Glaucidae
Glaucus atlanticus Forster, 1777

Order Steganobranchia
Family Bullidae
Bulla striata Bruguiére, 1792
Family Aplysiidae
Aplysia brasiliana Rang, 1828
Order Actophila
Family Ellobiidae
Melampus bidentatus Say, 1822
Order Hygrophila
Family Siphonariidae
Siphonaria pectinata (Linnaeus, 1758)
Class Bivalvia
Order Arcoidea
Family Arcidae
Anadara brasiliana (Lamarck, 1819)
Anadara ovalis (Bruguiére, 1789)
Arca imbricata Bruguiére, 1789
Noetia ponderosa (Say, 1822)
Order Mytiloidea
Family Mytilidae
Brachidontes exustus (Linnaeus, 1758)
Geukensia demissa granosissima (Sowerby, 1914)
Ischadium recurvum (Rafinesque, 1820)
Lithophaga aristata (Dillwyn, 1817)
Lithophaga bisulcata (d'Orbigny, 1845)
Family Pinnidae
Atrina seminuda (Lamarck, 1819)
Atrina serrata (Sowerby, 1825)
Order Pterioidea
Family Pteridae
Pteria colymbus (Roding, 1798)
Family Isognomonidae
Isognomon bicolor (C.B. Adams, 1845)
Family Pectinidae
Argopecten irradians amplicostatus (Dall, 1898)
Family Ostreidae
Crassostrea virginica Gmelin, 1792
Ostrea equestris Say, 1834
Order Veneroidea
Family Lucinidae
Lucina pectinata (Gmelin, 1791)
Order Hippuritoidea
Family Chamidae
Chama macerophylla Gmelin, 1791
Family Mactridae
Mulinia lateralis (Say, 1822)
Rangia cuneata (Gray, 1831)
Family Tellinidae
Macoma constricta (Bruguiére, 1792)
Macoma mitchelli Dall, 1895
Tellina alternata Say, 1822
Tellina lineata Turton, 1819
Tellina versicolor DeKay, 1843

Family Donacidae
  Donax texasiana Philippi, 1847
  Donax variabilis roemeri Philippi, 1849
Family Solecurtidae
  Tagelus plebeius (Solander, 1786)
Family Scrobiculariidae
  Abra aequalis (Say, 1822)
Family Veneridae
  Chione cancellata (Linnaeus, 1767)
  Chione grus (Holmes, 1858)
  Dosinia discus (Reeve, 1850)
  Mercenaria campechiensis texana (Dall, 1902)
Order Myoidea
  Family Myidae
    Paramya subovata (Conrad, 1845)
  Family Pholadidae
    Cyrtopleura costata (Linnaeus, 1758)
    Diplothyra smithii Tryon, 1862
  Family Teredinidae
    Bankia gouldi (Bartsch, 1908)
    Teredo bartschi Clapp, 1923
Class Scaphopoda
  Family Dentaliidae
    Dentalium texasianum Philippi, 1849
Class Cephalopoda
  Order Teuthoidea
    Family Loliginidae
      Loligo pealei Lesueur, 1821
      Lolliguncula brevis (Blainville, 1823)
  Order Octopoda
    Family Octopodidae
      Octopus vulgaris Linnaeus, 1758
Phylum Arthropoda
  Class Pantopoda
    Family Tanystylidae
      Tanystylum orbiculare Wilson, 1878
    Family Endeidae
      Endeis spinosa (Montagu, 1808)
  Class Merostomata
    Order Xiphosurida
      Family Limulidae
        Limulus polyphemus (Linnaeus, 1758)
  Class Crustacea
  Subclass Copepoda
    Family Acartiidae
      Acartia tonsa Dana, 1849
  Subclass Cirripedia
    Family Lepadidae
      Lepas anatifera Linnaeus, 1767
      Lepas anserifera Linnaeus, 1767
      Lepas pectinata Spengler, 1793
      Octolasmis lowei (Darwin, 1851)
    Family Chthamalidae
      Chthamalus fragilis Darwin, 1854

Family Balanidae
  Balanus amphitrite amphitrite Darwin, 1854
  Balanus venustus niveus Darwin, 1854
  Balanus reticulatus Utinomi, 1967
  Balanus tintinnabulum (Linnaeus, 1767)
  Balanus eburneus Gould, 1841
  Balanus improvisus Darwin, 1854
  Chelonibia patula (Ranzani, 1818)
  Chelonibia testudinaria Linnaeus, 1758

Subclass Malacostraca
  Order Stomatopoda
    Family Squillidae
      Squilla empusa Say, 1818
  Order Cumacea
    Family Diastylidae
      Oxyurostylis salinoi
  Order Tanaidacea
    Family Paratanaidae
      Leptochelia dubia (Krøyer, 1842)
  Order Isopoda
    Family Limnoridae
      Limnoria tripunctata Menzies, 1951
    Family Sphaeromidae
      Dynamene perforata Moore, 1902
      Sphaeroma quadridentatum Say, 1818
    Family Ligidae
      Ligia exotica (Roux, 1828)
    Family Bopyridae
      Bopyrissa wolffi Markham, 1978
  Order Amphipoda
    Family Ampeliscidae
      Ampelisca abdita Mills, 1964
    Family Bateidae
      Batea cartharinensis Müller, 1865
    Family Corophiidae
      Corophium acherusicum Costa, 1857
      Corophium louisianum Shoemaker, 1934
      Erichthonius brasiliensis (Dana, 1853)
    Family Gammaridae
      Gammarus mucronatus Say, 1818
    Family Ischyroceridae
      Jassa falcata (Montagu, 1808)
    Family Leucothoidae
      Leucothoe spinicarpa (Abildgaard, 1789)
    Family Oedicerotidae
      Synchelidium americanum Bousfield, 1973
    Family Talitridae
      Orchestia grillus Bosc, 1802
  Order Caprellidea
    Family Caprellidae
      Caprella equilibra Say, 1818
  Order Mysidacea
    Family Mysidae
      Mysidopsis almyra Bowman, 1964

Order Decapoda
  Family Penaeidae
    Parapenaeus longirostris (Lucas, 1849)
    Penaeus aztecus Ives, 1891
    Penaeus duorarum Burkenroad, 1939
    Penaeus setiferus (Linnaeus, 1767)
    Sicyonia dorsalis Kingsley, 1878
    Trachypeneus constrictus Stimpson, 1871
    Trachypeneus similis (Smith,
    Xiphopeneus krøyeri Heller, 1862
  Family Sergestidae
    Acetes americanus louisianensis Burken-road, 1934
    Lucifer faxoni Borradaile, 1915
  Family Pasiphaeidae
    Leptochela serratorbita Bate, 1888
  Family Palaemonidae
    Palaemonetes pugio Holthuis, 1949
    Palaemonetes vulgaris (Say, 1818)
  Family Alpheidae
    Alpheus heterochaelis Say, 1818
    Synalpheus fritzmeulleri Coutiere, 1909
  Family Ogyrididae
    Ogyrides limicola Williams, 1955
  Family Hippolytidae
    Hippolysmata wurdemanni Gibbes, 1850
    Hippolyte pleuracantha (Stimpson, 1871)
    Latreutes fucorum (Fabricius, 1798)
    Latreutes parvulus (Stimpson, 1866)
    Tozeuma carolinense Kingsley, 1878
  Family Scyllaridae
    Scyllarides nodifer (Stimpson, 1866)
  Family Callianassidae
    Callianassa jamaicense louisianensis Schmitt, 1935
  Family Diogenidae
    Clibanarius vittatus (Bosc, 1802)
    Dardanus fucosus Biffar & Provenzano, 1972
    Isocheles wurdemanni Stimpson, 1862
    Paguristes puncticeps Benedict, 1901
    Petrochirus diogenes (Linnaeus, 1758)
  Family Paguridae
    Pagurus annulipes (Stimpson, 1862)
    Pagurus bonairensis Schmitt, 1936
    Pagurus impressus (Benedict, 1892)
    Pagurus longicarpus Say, 1817
    Pagurus pollicaris Say, 1817
  Family Procellanidae
    Euceramus praelongus Stimpson, 1860
    Petrolisthes armatus (Gibbes, 1850)
    Porcellana sayana (Leach, 1820)
  Family Hippidae
    Emerita portoricensis Schmitt, 1935

  Family Albuneidae
    Albunea paretii Guérin, 1853
    Lepidopa websteri Benedict, 1903
  Family Raninidae
    Raninoides louisianensis Rathbun, 1933
  Family Calippidae
    Calappa sulcata Rathbun, 1898
    Hepatus epheliticus (Linnaeus, 1763)
  Family Leucosiidae
    Persephona aquilonaris Rathbun, 1933
  Family Dromiidae
    Dromidia antillensis Stimpson, 1858
  Family Majidae
    Libinia dubia Milne-Edwards, 1834
    Libinia emarginata Leach, 1815
    Stenorynchus seticornis (Herbst, 1788)
  Family Portunidae
    Arenaeus cribrarius (Lamarck, 1818)
    Callinectes marginatus Milne-Edwards, 1861
    Callinectes ornatus Ordway, 1863
    Callinectes sapidus Rathbun, 1896
    Cronius ruber (Lamarck, 1818)
    Ovalipes quadulpensis (Saussure, 1858)
    Portunus gibbesii (Stimpson, 1859)
    Portunus sayi (Gibbes, 1850)
    Portunus spinimanus (Latreille, 1819)
  Family Xanthidae
    Eurypanopeus depressus (Smith, 1869)
    Hexapanopeus paulensis Rathbun, 1930
    Menippe mercenaria (Say, 1818)
    Neopanope texana texana (Stimpson, 1859)
    Panopeus herbstii Milne-Edwards, 1834
    Panopeus turgidus Rathbun, 1930
    Pilumnus dasypodus Kingsley, 1879
    Pilumnus pannosus Rathbun, 1897
    Pseudomedaeus agassizi (A. Milne-Edwards, 1880)
    Rithropanopeus harrisii (Gould, 1841)
  Family Pinnotheridae
    Pinnotheres maculatus Say, 1818
    Pinnotheres ostreum Say, 1817
    Pinnixa chaetopterana Stimpson, 1860
    Pinnixa lunzi Glassell, 1937
  Family Grapsidae
    Pachygrapsus transversus (Gibbes, 1850)
    Sesarma cinereum (Bosc, 1801 or 1802)
    Sesarma reticulatum (Say, 1817)
  Family Gecarcinidae
    Cardisoma guanhumi Latreille, 1825
    Gecarcinus lateralis (Freminville, 1835)
  Family Ocypodidae
    Ocypode quadrata (Fabricius, 1787)
    Uca longisignalis Salmon & Atsaides, 1968
    Uca minax (Le Conte, 1955)

Uca panaceae Salmon, 1974
Uca rapax (Smith, 1870)
Uca subcylindrica (Stimpson, 1859)
Phylum Sipuncula
Phascolion strombi (Montagu, 1804)
Phylum Echiura
Family Thalassemidae
Thalassema hartmani Fisher, 1947
Phylum Phoronida
Phoronis architecta Andrews, 1890
Phylum Brachiopoda
Family Lingulidae
Glottidia pyramidata (Stimpson, 1860)
Phylum Bryozoa
Class Gymnolaemata
Order Cheilostomata
Family Aeteidae
Aetea anguina (Linnaeus, 1758)
Family Membraniporidae
Membranipora commensale (Kirkpatrick & Metzelaar, 1922)
Membranipora savartii (Audouin, 1826)
Membranipora tenuis Desor, 1848
Family Bugulidae
Bugula neritina (Linnaeus, 1758)
Bugula rylandi Maturo, 1966
Family Schizoporellidae
Schizoporella errata (Waters, 1878)
Family Smittinidae
Parasmittina trispinosa (Johnson)
Family Savignyellidae
Savignyella lafonti (Audouin)
Phylum Echinodermata
Class Asteroidea
Order Platyasterida
Family Luidiidae
Luidia alternata (Say, 1825)
Luidia clathrata (Say, 1825)
Order Paxillosida
Family Astropectinidae
Astropecten duplicatus Gray, 1840

Class Ophiuroidea
Order Ophiurida
Family Amphiuridae
Hemipholis elongata (Say, 1825)
Micropholis atra (Stimpson, 1852)
Ophiactis savignyi (Müller & Troschel, 1842)
Ophiophragmus moorei Thomas, 1965
Family Ophiothrichidae
Ophiothrix angulata (Say, 1825)
Class Echinoidea
Order Diadematoida
Family Diadematidae
Diadema antillarum Philippi, 1845
Order Arbacoida
Family Arbaciidae
Arbacia punctulata (Lamarck, 1816)
Order Echinoida
Family Echinometridae
Echinometra lucunter (Linnaeus, 1758)
Order Clypeasteroida
Family Mellitidae
Mellita quinquiesperforata (Leske, 1778)
Class Holothuroidea
Order Dendrochirotida
Family Cucumariidae
Thyone mexicana Deichmann, 1946
Phylum Chaetognatha
Sagitta tenuis Conant, 1896
Phylum Chordata
Class Ascidiacea
Order Pleurogona
Family Molgulidae
Molgula manhattensis (DeKay, 1843)
Class Larvacea
Family Oikopleuridae
Oikopleura sp.
Class Cephalochordata
Branchiostoma caribaeum Sundevall, 1853

Glossary

abalone   A limpetlike gastropod whose large foot is considered a delicacy in California and Japan.

adductor muscle   The large muscle of a clam or scallop that closes the shell upon contraction.

amphipod   A small crustacean with a laterally compressed body and usually having enlarged hind legs for jumping. Beach fleas, *Orchestia, Gammarus.*

anisomyarian   Having adductor muscles that are not equal in size.

antenna (pl. **antennae**)   A sensory appendage found on the head, e.g. the "feeler" of a lobster or insect.

antennal scale   Bladelike projection from the base of the antenna of certain crustaceans, e.g. *Squilla.*

antennule   One of the more anterior pair of antennae in crustaceans possessing two pairs of antennae.

autotomize   To self-amputate a part of the body, such as a leg or tail, usually to facilitate escape.

avicularium   A small defensive heterozooid in some bryozoans.

benthic   Living on or in the sediments of aquatic habitats, as opposed to *pelagic.*

berried   Carrying eggs on the outside of the body like a large mass of minute berries. *See also* gravid.

bryozoan   A moss animal; a member of the phylum Bryozoa.

budding   A method of asexual reproduction in which a new individual arises as an outgrowth of its parent.

byssus (or **byssal threads**)   The tuft of fibers produced by mussels, ark clams and a few other bivalves to anchor themselves to the substrate.

carapace   The top portion of a crustacean's external skeleton, e.g. the broad, flat "shell" of a blue crab.

carina   A ridge, or keel, commonly found on the exoskeletons of certain arthropods.

carpus   The third segment from the tip of a shrimp or crab leg, often forming an elbow.

carrion   The dead body or carcass of an animal, such as a fish or crab, that is washed up on the beach.

cercaria (pl. **cercariae**)   The free-swimming larval stage of a fluke. *See also* trematode.

chela (pl. **chelae**)   A claw found on the first pair of legs of some crustaceans.

cheliped   A leg that bears a claw, as in the blue crab or lobster.

chemoreception   The reception of chemical stimuli, such as those produced by food or pollutants in the water; corresponds to senses of taste and smell.

chitin   A protein that is used to form the shells of crustaceans.

chromatophore   A pigment-containing cell, especially one with branching processes which enable the pigment to be dispersed or concentrated.

cilia (sing. **cilium**)   Minute, hairlike structures whose beating aids in locomotion, feeding and/or transport of wastes.

ciliary mucous feeder   Organism that traps suspended food in mucous and transports the mixture to its mouth on cilia.

cirrus (pl. **cirri**)   A flexible projection from the body of an animal, usually contributing to a sense of touch.

commensal   A relationship between organisms of different species that live together in a close association.

conchiolin   A protein used to form a matrix in which calcite and aragonite are embedded to form the shell of a snail or clam.

copepod   A minute crustacean with very long antennae; a dominant animal in the zooplankton.

cosmopolitan   Having a worldwide distribution.

coxal plate   A flattened extension of the basal segment of an amphipod leg that gives the bearer the appearance of being armour plated.

crustacean   A group of aquatic animals characterized by jointed legs and a hard shell which is shed periodically, e.g. shrimp, crabs, crayfish, isopods and amphipods.

ctenodont   A comblike tooth structure found in the hinge teeth of some bivalves.

ctenophore   A nonstinging "jellyfish" characterized by eight rows of cilia which propel it through the water.

cuticle   A noncellular membrane that covers the epidermis on many invertebrates.

cypris   A free-swimming larval form of barnacles.

dactylozooid   A protective individual in a hydroid colony.

deposit feeder   An animal that derives nourishment by swallowing mud or sand and digesting whatever food particles may be present.

diatom A unicellular plant possessing a siliceous shell.

ectoparasite A parasite that lives on the surface of its host.

epipodite A branch from the basal segment of a crustacean leg that often functions as a gill.

epithelium A tissue lining the surfaces of gland ducts and cavities.

epitoky A reproductive phenomenon occurring in certain polychaete worms in which the anterior asexual portion (the atoke) differs from the posterior portion (the epitoke) of the worm.

errant Wandering, as in certain active worms which continually crawl through the sand or mud. Prone to traveling.

estuary An area at the intersection of a river and the sea where seawater and freshwater are mixed, producing brackish water.

euryhaline Tolerant of a wide range of salinities. A property of most estuarine animals.

evisceration Discharge of the internal organs in sea cucumbers.

filter-feeder An animal that derives nourishment by screening small organisms or other food particles from the water.

flotsam Wreckage of a ship or its cargo especially when cast up on the shore. Usually refers to any form of driftwood or other nonliving object adrift.

fouling organism A sessile organism living where it is unwanted, e.g. barnacles on a ship's hull.

freshet A short, heavy rainstorm which causes a large amount of fresh water to enter the marine environment.

gastrozooid A feeding individual in a hydroid colony.

gemmule A resistant asexual reproductive body found in freshwater and some marine sponges.

gonopore An opening through which sperm or eggs leave an animal's body.

gonozooid A reproductive individual in a hydroid colony.

gorgonian A soft coral, e.g. a sea whip or sea fan, of the order Gorgonacea.

gravid Bearing eggs, e.g. the "sponge crab" stage of a blue crab. *See also* berried.

groin A short breakwater usually constructed in rows perpendicular to the beach to impede longshore currents which would erode the beach.

halophyte A plant that is tolerant of a high salt concentration in the soil.

hermaphroditic Monoecious; having both male and female sex organs.

holoplankton Organisms that spend their entire life cycles suspended in the water.

hydroid The polypoid or anemonelike form of a member of the class Hydrozoa.

hydrotheca Chitinous protective case around a feeding zooid on a hydrozoan colony.

hypersaline Having a salt content higher than that of normal seawater (> 35.0‰).

integument The surface covering of an animal's body.

interstitial Living in the spaces between mud or sand particles. *See also* pore space.

introvert Neck-like region in many sipunculids which can be inverted into the trunk of the body.

isomyarian Having adductor muscles that are equal in size.

isopod A small flattened crustacean belonging to the order Isopoda.

jetsam Anything jettisoned from a ship in distress and subsequently washed ashore.

larva (*pl.* **larvae**) An embryo that differs markedly in appearance from its parents and becomes self-sustaining before assuming the physical characteristics of its parents.

littoral Intertidal; pertaining to the shore zone between the high and low tide levels.

littorine A snail of the genus *Littorina*. *See also* periwinkle.

lophophore Spiralled crown of tentacles used for food capture in bryozoans, brachiopods and phoronids.

lunule A notch or hole in a sand dollar test.

malacologist A biologist who specializes in the study of mollusks.

mantle A fold of tissue in the mollusks and a few other animals that is nearest the shell and is responsible for depositing the layers of shell.

mantle cavity A space formed between the mantle and the body of mollusks usually containing the gills.

maxilliped A crustacean thoracic appendage usually used in handling food.

medusa (pl. **medusae**) The "jellyfish" stage in the life cycles of certain Hydrozoa and their kin. Usually appears as a gelatinous bell with trailing tentacles. *See also* hydroid, polyp.

megalops A free-swimming larval stage of crabs that follows the zoea stage.

meroplankton Organisms that spend a portion of their life cycles suspended in the water.

MLLW Mean lower low water: water level during the lower of two daily low tides occurring in areas with semi-diurnal tides.

molt To shed one's outer covering (feathers, skin or shell) during growth. The outer covering that has been shed.

morphology The form or structure of an animal or plant.

mysid A small, shrimplike crustacean belonging to the order Mysidacea.

mysis A larval stage in the life history of shrimp.

nauplius The first larval stage of certain crustaceans, such as shrimp.

nekton Pelagic animals capable of swimming faster than one knot (one nautical mile/hour).

nematocyst A stinging or grasping structure used for food capture and defense in medusae, sea anemones, and their kin.

nematophore Nematocyst-bearing defensive structure on certain hydrozoan colonies.

nudibranch A type of snail that lacks a shell and often has fingerlike or lobelike projections on its back.

odontophore A cartilagelike structure that supports the radula of a snail.

operculum A lid or plug used to close an opening, as in many snails and some polychaete worms.

opisthobranch A snail belonging to the subclass Opisthobranchia.

osculum Large, excurrent pore in a sponge.

osmoconformer An organism that adjusts to changes in the salinity of its environment by changing the salinity of its body fluid accordingly.

parapodium (pl. **parapodia**) A segmental appendage on a polychaete worm. May be leglike or variously modified as a gill, pump, etc.

pedicle Stalk used to anchor a brachiopod in sand or to a hard substrate.

pelagic Living suspended in the water, as opposed to *benthic.*

penis (pl. **penes**) A male copulatory organ.

pereiopod A crustacean thoracic leg on which crabs, shrimp, isopods and their kin walk.

periostracum The horny layer that coats the exterior surface of the shells of most mollusks.

perisarc A thin chitinous layer covering a hydroid colony.

periwinkle A snail of the genus *Littorina. See also* littorine.

permeable Capable of being penetrated by water and certain ions. An animal with a permeable integument will dry out easily in an arid environment.

phytoplankton Plant plankton; generally microscopic plants adrift in the sea.

plankter An individual member of the plankton.

planula A free-swimming larva of certain hydroids and their kin.

pleopod An abdominal appendage on a crustacean, which may be used for swimming, respiration or holding eggs.

podium (pl. **podia**) A small foot, usually terminating in a sucker, found on sea stars, sea urchins, sand dollars and their kin.

polyp The sessile or anemonelike stage in the life cycles of certain Cnidaria. Usually appears as an attached stalk with a crown of tentacles. *See also* medusa.

pore space The space in between particles of sand or mud. It provides a habitat for a variety of microscopic organisms. *See also* interstitial.

postlarva The last larval stage in the life history of shrimp.

proboscis Usually a tubelike extension of the mouth of a snail or worm which can either be shot out to grab passing prey or extended into narrow crevices after food.

propodium The anterior portion of the foot of certain snails, such as the moon snail.

prosobranch A snail belonging to the subclass Prosobranchia.

prostomium Anterior segment in an annelid worm, usually modified as a head.

protandry In individual organisms bearing both male and female gonads, the male reproductive system matures and atrophies, before the maturation of the female system.

protozoea A larval stage in the life history of certain crustaceans that follows the nauplius larva and precedes the zoea larva.

pseudofeces A mixture of mucous and particles rejected by certain filter-feeders before ingestion, as in the oyster.

pulmonate A snail which lacks gills and must exchange gases across the wall of the mantle cavity. Usually terrestrial or freshwater species.

radiole A pinnate tentaclelike projection from the head of certain filter-feeding polychaete worms, such as fanworms.

radula A ribbonlike band bearing many rows of teeth found in the mouth of many mollusks.

raptorial leg A leg adapted for seizing and tearing prey.

rhopalium (pl. **rhopalia**) A structure containing various sense organs found on the margin of a medusa's bell.

rostrum A beaklike projection from the carapace of certain crustaceans, such as shrimp and crayfish, that extends forward between the eyes.

scyphistoma A polyplike stage in the life history of certain medusae which develops into free-swimming ephyra larvae by strobilization. *See also* strobilization.

sessile Sedentary; permanently attached to a rock, shell or other firm substrate.

seta (pl. **setae**) A stiff bristle or hairlike structure found on the bodies of certain worms and crustaceans; usually tactile.

shoal A shallow place, such as a sand bar, in a body of water.

siphon A tube used to channel the flow of water in many mollusks and sea squirts.

spat Newly settled oysters.

spermatophore A packet of spermatozoa which is transferred to the female in certain mollusks and crustaceans.

spicule Calcareous or siliceous skeletal component in some sponges and gorgonians.

statocyst An equilibrium organ consisting of an inorganic weight, the statolith, which is balanced on numerous sensory hairs.

stenohaline Tolerant of only a very narrow range of salinities. A property of most truly marine animals.

stolon A rootlike outgrowth from the base of certain cnidarians that produces new individuals by budding.

strobilization A form of asexual reproduction in the phylum Cnidaria in which eplyra larvae are budded off of a polyp. *See also* scyphistoma.

subchelate Forming a grasping appendage by folding the terminal segment of a leg back over the subterminal segment.

substrate The base or foundation on which an animal lives or moves, e.g. the ground or a plant stalk.

tactile Pertaining to a sense of touch.

telson The last body segment of most crustaceans, often part of the tail fan or modified for digging or protecting eggs.

test The skeleton of a sea urchin or sand dollar.

thixotropy The property of becoming fluid when agitated, as in wet sand or mud.

trematode A fluke or parasitic flatworm.

trilobite An extinct marine arthropod that inhabited Paleozoic seas and had a three-lobed carapace.

trochophore A larval stage found in the mollusks and a few other animal groups that is characterized by two large lobes containing cilia whose beating simulates the action of an egg-beater to propel the trochophore and bring it in contact with food particles.

tube foot *See* podium.

umbilicus A depression in the shells of certain snails, such as the moon snail, around which the shell coils.

varix (pl. **varices**) A prominant ridge across the shell of certain snails (e.g. *Cerithidea*) which represents a previous position of the lip of the shell.

water table The water level in beach sand or soil characterized by a layer of moist sand or mud.

whelk A common name applied to certain snails, e.g. *Busycon*.

zoea (pl. **zoeae**) A larval stage in the life history of certain crustaceans, such as shrimp.

zooid An individual member of colony of animals, such as a hydroid colony or a bryozoan colony.

zooplankton Animal plankton; usually small animals adrift in the sea that are unable to swim against a one knot current.

Bibliography

General Reading

Abbott, R.T. 1954. *American Seashells*. New York: Van Nostrand.

Amos, W.H. 1966. *The Life of the Seashore*. New York: McGraw-Hill.

Andrews, J. 1977. *Shells and Shores of Texas*. Austin: Univ. of Texas Press.

Andrews, J. 1971. *Sea Shells of the Texas Coast*. Austin: Univ. of Texas Press.

Arnold, A.F. 1968. *The Sea-beach at Ebb-tide*. New York: Dover.

Eltringham, S.K. 1971. *Life in Mud and Sand*. New York: Crane, Russak & Co.

Evans, I.O. (Ed.). 1962. *Sea and Seashore*. New York: Warne.

Green, J. 1968. *The Biology of Estuarine Animals*. London: Sidgwick & Jackson.

Hardy, A.C. 1956. *The Open Sea*. Boston: Houghton Mifflin.

Jagersten, G. 1964. *Life in the Sea*. New York: Basic Books.

Le Danois, E. 1957. *Marine Life of Coastal Waters*. Harrap.

Marshall, N.B. 1971. *Ocean Life*. New York: MacMillan.

Miner, R.W. 1950. *Field Book of Seashore Life*. New York: G.P. Putnam's Sons.

Newell, R.C. 1970. *Biology of Intertidal Animals*. New York: American Elsevier.

Reed, C.T. 1941. *Marine Life in Texas Waters*. Houston: Anson Jones Press.

Rudloe, J. 1968. *The Sea Brings Forth*. New York: Alfred A. Knopf.

Rudloe, J. 1971. *The Erotic Ocean*. New York: World Publ. Co.

Russell, F.S., and C.M. Yonge. 1963. *The Seas: Our Knowledge of Life in the Sea and How it is Gained*. New York: Warne.

Teal, J.M., and M. Teal. 1969. *Life and Death of the Salt Marsh*. Boston: Little, Brown & Co.

Wilson, D.P. 1952. *Life of the Shore and Shallow Sea*. New York: McBride.

Wimpenny, R.S. 1966. *The Plankton of the Sea*. New York: American Elsevier.

Yonge, C.M. 1963. *The Sea Shore*. New York: Atheneum.

Zim, H.S., and L. Ingle. 1955. *Seashores*. New York: Golden Press.

Porifera

Cobb, W.R. 1969. "Penetration of calcium carbonate substrates by the boring sponge, *Cliona*," *Amer. Zool.* 9:783-790.

de Laubenfels, M.W. 1953. "Sponges from the Gulf of Mexico," *Bull. Mar. Sci.* 2:511-557.

Elvin, D.W. 1976. "Seasonal growth and reproduction of an intertidal sponge, *Haliclona permollis* (Bowerbank)." *Biol. Bull.* 151:108-125.

Fell, P.E. 1976. "The reproduction of *Haliclona loosanoffi* and its apparent relationship to water temperature." *Biol. Bull.* 150:200-210.

Hopkins, S.H. 1956. "Notes on the boring sponges in the Gulf Coast estuaries and their relation to salinity," *Bull. Mar. Sci.* 6:44-58.

Storr, J.F. 1976. "Ecological factors controlling sponge distribution in the Gulf of Mexico and the resulting zonation." *In* Harrison, F.W. and R.R. Cowden (eds.), *Aspects of Sponge Biology*. New York: Academic Press.

Teerling, J. 1975. "A survey of sponges from the northwestern Gulf of Mexico." Ph.D. Diss., Univ. Southwestern Louisiana. x + 187 p.

Wells, H.W., M.J. Wells, and I.E. Gray. 1960. "Marine sponges of North Carolina." *J. Elisha Mitchell Sci. Soc.* 76:200-245.

Cnidaria

Ballard, W.W. 1942. "The mechanism for synchronous spawning in *Hydractinia* and *Pennaria*," *Biol. Bull.* 82:329-339.

Bayer, F.M. 1961. Studies on the fauna of Curacao and other Caribbean Islands: No. 55. The shallow-water Octocorallia of the West Indian Region. Vol. 12. Natuurwet. Stud. Suriname No. 23 1961:1-373.

Burke, W.D. 1976. "Biology and distribution of the macrocoelenterates of Mississippi Sound and adjacent waters." *Gulf Res. Repts.* 5:17-28.

Cargo, D.G., and L.P. Schultz. 1966. "Notes on the biology of the sea nettle, *Chrysaora quinquecirrha*, in Chesapeake Bay," *Chesapeake Sci.* 7:95-100.

Cargo, D.G., and L.P. Schultz. 1967. "Further observations on the biology of the sea nettle and jellyfishes in Chesapeake Bay." *Chesapeake Sci.* 8:209-220.

Carlgren, O., and J.W. Hedgpeth. 1952. "Actinaria, Zoantharia and Ceriantharia from the shallow water in the northwestern Gulf of Mexico," *Publ. Inst. Mar. Sci. Texas* 2:143-172.

Cones, H.N., Jr. 1968. "Strobilation of *Chrysaora quinquecirrha* polyps in the laboratory," *Vir. J. Sci.* 20:16-18.

Cones, H.N., Jr., and D.S. Haven. 1969. "Distribution of *Chrysaora quinquecirrha* in the York River," *Chesapeake Sci.* 10:75-84.

Cowles, P.R. 1920. "The transplanting of sea anemones by hermit crabs," Proc. Natn. Acad. Sci. U.S. 6:40-42.

Cutress, C., and D.M. Ross. 1969. "The sea anemone *Calliactis tricolor* (LeSueur) and its association with the hermit crab *Dardanus venosus* (H. Milne-Edwards)," *J. Zool.* 158:225-241.

Cutress, C., D.M. Ross, and L. Sutton. 1970. "The association of *Calliactis tricolor* with its pagurid, calappid, and majid partners in the Caribbean," *Can. J. Zool.* 48:371-376.

Deevey, E.S. 1950. "Hydroids from Louisiana and Texas, with remarks on the Pleistocene biogeography of the western Gulf of Mexico." *Ecology* 31:334-367.

Defenbaugh, R.E., and S.H. Hopkins. 1973. "The occurrence and distribution of the hydroids of the Galveston Bay, Texas area," *Texas A&M Univ. Sea Grant Publ.* TAMU-SG-73-210.

Edwards, C. 1966. "*Velella velella* (L.): the distribution of its dimorphic forms in the Atlantic Ocean and the Mediterranean, with comments on its nature and affinities." In Barnes, H. (Ed.). Some contemporary studies in marine science, pp. 283-296. Allen & Unwin Ltd.

Field, L.R. 1949. "Sea anemones and corals of Beaufort, North Carolina," *Duke Univ. Mar. Sta. Bull.* 5:1-39.

Fraser, J.H. 1969. "Experimental feeding of some medusae and chaetognatha," *J. Fish. Res. Bd. Canada* 26:1743-1762.

Guest, W.C. 1959. "The occurrence of the jellyfish *Chiropsalmus quadrumanus* in Matagorda Bay, Texas," *Bull. Mar. Sci.* 9:79-83.

Gutsell, J.S. 1928. "The spider crab, *Libinia dubia*, and the jellyfish, *Stomolophus meleagris*, found associated at Beaufort, N.C.," *Ecology* 9:358-359.

Jachowski, R. 1963. "Observations on the moon jelly, *Aurelia aurita*, and the spider crab, *Libinia dubia*," *Chesapeake Sci.* 4:195.

Kornicker, L.S., and J.T. Conover. 1960. "Effect of high storm tide levels on beach burial of jellyfish (Scyphozoa) and other organisms," *Int. Rev. Hydrobiol.* 45:203-214.

Kramp, P.L. 1961. "Synopsis of the medusae of the world," *J. Mar. Biol. Assoc. U.K.* 40:1-469.

Kramp, P.L. 1965. "The hydromedusae of the Atlantic Ocean and adjacent water," *Dana Rept.* 49:159.

Lane, C.E., and E. Dodge. 1958. "The toxicity of *Physalia* nematocysts," *Biol. Bull.* 115:219-226.

Leversee, G.J. 1976. "Flow and feeding in fan-shaped colonies of the gorgonian coral, *Leptogorgia*." *Biol. Bull.* 151:344-356.

Littleford, R.A., and R.V. Truitt. 1937. "Variation of *Dactylometra quinquecirrha*," *Science* 86:426-427.

Marsical, R.N. 1972. "The nature of the adhesion to shells of the symbiotic sea anemone *Calliactis tricolor* (LeSueur)," *J. Exp. Mar. Biol. Ecol.* 8:217-224.

McNamara, P. 1955. "Sea nettles observed to feed on sea walnuts in laboratory," *Maryland Tidewater News* 12:3.

Merrill, A.S. 1968. "Shell deformity of mollusks attributable to the hydroid, *Hydractinia echinata*," *U.S. Fish Wildl. Serv. Fish. Bull.* 66:273-279.

Mills, C.E. 1976. "*Podocoryne selena*, a new species of hydroid from the Gulf of Mexico, and a comparison with *Hydractinia echinata*." *Biol. Bull.* 151:214-224.

Phillips, P.J., W.D. Burke, and E.L. Keener. 1969. "Observations on the trophic significance of jellyfishes in Mississippi Sound with quantitative data on the associative behavior of small fishes with medusae," *Trans. Amer. Fish. Soc.* 98:703-712.

Singer, J. 1968. "Man against jellyfish," *Sea Frontiers* 14:87-93.

Thompson, T.E., and I. Bennett. 1969. "*Physalia* nematocysts: utilized by mollusks for defense," *Science* 166:1532-1533.

Wilson, D.P. 1947. "The Portuguese man-of-war, *Physalia physalis* L., in British and adjacent seas," *J. Mar. Biol. Assoc.* U.K. 27:139-172.

Woodcock, A.H. 1956. "Dimorphism in the Portuguese man-of-war," *Nature.* Lond. 178:253-255.

Ctenophora

Bishop, J.W. 1967. "Feeding rates of the ctenophore, *Mnemiopsis leidyi*," *Chesapeake Sci.* 8:259-264.

Cronin, L.E., J.D. Daiber, and E.M. Hulbert. 1962. "Quantitative seasonal aspects of zooplankton in the Delaware River Estuary," *Chesapeake Sci.* 3:63-93.

Mayer, A.G. 1912. "Ctenophores of the Atlantic Coast of North America," *Carnegie Inst. Wash. Publ.* 162: 1-58.

Nelson, T.C. 1925. "On the occurrence and food habits of ctenophores in New Jersey coastal waters," *Biol. Bull.* 48:92-111.

Platyhelminthes

Hopkins, S.H. 1949. "Preliminary survey of the literature on *Stylochus* and other flatworms associated with oysters," Texas A&M Res. Found. Proj. 9:1-16.

Hyman, L.H. 1940. "The polyclad flatworms of the Atlantic Coast of the United States and Canada," Proc. U.S. Natn. Mus. 89:449-495.

Pearse, A.S. 1949. "Observations on flatworms and nemerteans collected at Beaufort, N.C.," Proc. U.S. Natn. Mus. 100:25-37.

Pearse, A.S., and G.W. Wharton. 1938. "The oyster "leech" *Stylochus inimicus* Palombi, associated with oysters on the coasts of Florida," *Ecol. Monogr.* 8:605-655.

Polychaeta

Barnes, R.D. 1965. "Tube-building and feeding in chaetopterid polychaetes." *Biol. Bull.* 129:217-233.

Bishop, J. 1974. "Observations on the swarming of a nereid polychaete, *Neanthes succinea*, from the northern Gulf of Mexico." *Proc. La. Acad. Sci.* 37:60-63.

Blake, J.A., and J.W. Evans. 1973. "*Polydora* and related genera as borers in mollusk shells and other calcareous substrates (Polychaeta: Spionidae)," *Veliger* 15:235-249.

Brown, S.C., J.B. Bdzil, and H.L. Frisch. 1972. "Responses of *Chaetopterus variopedatus* to osmotic stress, with a discussion of the mechanism of isoosmotic volume-regulation," *Biol. Bull.* 143:278-295.

Dales, R.P. 1957. "The feeling mechanism and structure of the gut of *Owenia fusiformis*." *J. Mar. Biol. Assoc. U.K.* 36:81-89.

Daly, J.M. 1973. "Behavioral and secretory activity during tube construction by *Platynereis dumerilii*. Aud. & M. Edw. (Polychaeta: Nereidae)." *J. Mar. Biol. Assoc. U.K.* 53:521-529.

Dean, D. 1978. "The swimming of bloodworms (*Glycera* spp.) at night, with comments on other species." *Mar. Biol.* 48:99-104.

Evans, S.M. 1973. "A study of fighting reactions in some nereid polychaetes. *Anim. Behav.* 21:138-146.

Fauchald, K. 1977. "The polychaete worms: definitions and keys to the orders, families and genera." Natural History Museum of Los Angeles County, Science Series. 28:1-190.

Grassle, J.F., and J.P. Grassle. 1974. "Opportunistic life histories and genetic systems in marine benthic polychaetes." *J. Mar. Res.* 32:253-284.

Gray, I.E. 1961. "Changes in abundance of the commensal crabs of *Chaetopterus*," *Biol. Bull.* 120:353-359.

Haigler, S.A. 1969. "Boring mechanism of *Polydora websteri* inhabiting *Crassostrea virginica*," *Amer. Zool.* 9:821-828.

Hartman, O. 1951. "The littoral marine annelids of the Gulf of Mexico," *Publ. Inst. Mar. Sci.* 2:7-124.

Hopkins, S.H. 1958. "The planktonic larvae of *Polydora websteri* Hartman (Annelida: Polychaeta) and their settling on oysters," *Bull. Mar. Sci.* 8:268-277.

Hubbard, G.F. 1977. "A quantitative analysis of benthic polychaetous annelids from the northwestern Gulf of Mexico." M.S. Thesis, Texas A&M Univ. vi + 85 p.

Jones, M.L. 1963. "Four new species of *Magelona* (Annelida, Polychaeta) and a redescription of *Magelona longicornis* Johnson." *Amer. Mus. Novit.* 2164:1-31.

Mackin, J.G. and F. Cauthron. 1952. "Effect of heavy infestations of *Polydora websteri* Hartman on *Crassostrea virginica* (Gmelin) in Louisiana," Conv. Natl. Shellfish. Assoc. for 1952:14-24.

Mangum, C.P. 1964. "Activity patterns in metabolism and ecology of polychaetes." *Comp. Biochem. Physiol.* 11:239-256.

Mangum, C.P. 1964. "Studies on speciation in maldanid polychaetes of the North American Atlantic coast. II. Distribution and competitive interaction of five sympatric species." *Limnol. Oceanogr.* 9:12-26.

Mangum, C.P., S.L. Santos, and W.R. Rhodes, Jr. 1968. "Distribution and feeding in the onuphid polychaete, *Diopatra cuprea* (Bosc)." *Mar. Biol.* 2:33-40.

McCarty, D.M. 1974. "Polychaetes of Seven and One-Half Fathom Reef." M.S. Thesis, Texas A&I Univ. 213 p.

Myers, A.C. 1972. "Tube-worm sediment relationships of *Diopatra cuprea*," *Mar. Biol.* 17:350-356.

Pettibone, M.H. 1965. "Two new species of *Aricidea* (Polychaeta, Paraonidae) from Virginia and Florida, and redescription of *Aricidea fragilis* Webster." *Proc. Biol. Soc. Wash.* 78:127-139.

Truman, E.R. 1966. "The mechanism of burrowing in the polychaete worm, *Arenicola marina* (L.)," *Biol. Bull.* 131:369-377.

Wilson, D. 1969. "Honeycomb worm," *J. Mar. Biol. Assoc.* U.K. 15:567-604.

Gastropoda

Apley, M.L. 1970. "Field studies on life history, gonadal cycle and reproductive periodicity in *Melampus bidentatus* (Pulmonata: Ellobiidae)," *Malacologica* 10:381-397.

Bayer, F.M. 1963. "Observations on pelagic mollusks associated with the siphonophores *Velella* and *Physalia*," *Bull. Mar. Sci.* 13:454-466.

Butler, P.A. 1953. "The southern oyster drill," Natn. Shellfish. Assoc. 1953 Conv. Papers: 67-75.

Chapman, C.R. 1955. "Feeding habits of the southern oyster drill, *Thais haemastoma*," Proc. Natn. Shellfish. Assoc. for 1955:169-176.

Carriker, M.R. 1972. "Observations on removal of spines by muricid gastropods during shell growth," Veliger 15:69-74.

Craig, A.K. et al. 1969. "The gastropod, *Siphonaria pectinata*: a factor in destruction of beach rock," *Amer. Zool.* 9:895-901.

D'Asaro, C.N. 1966. "The egg capsules, embryogenesis, and early organogenesis of a common oyster predator, *Thais haemastoma floridana* (Gastropoda: Prosobranchia)," *Bull. Mar. Sci.* 16:884-914.

D'Asaro, C.N. 1970. "Egg capsules of prosobranch mollusks from South Florida and the Bahamas and notes on spawning in the laboratory," *Bull. Mar. Sci.* 20:414-440.

Demoran, W.J., and G. Gunter. 1956. "Ability of *Thais haemastoma* to regenerate its drilling mechanism," *Science* 123:1126.

Epstein, R.A. 1972. "Larval trematodes of marine gastropods of Galveston Island, Texas," M.Sc. Thesis. Texas A&M Univ.

Gore, R.H. 1966. "Observations on the escape response in *Nassarius vibex* (Say) (Mollusca: Gastropoda)," *Bull. Mar. Sci.* 16:423-434.

Gould, H.N. 1949. "The effects of temperature on growth and sexual changes in *Crepidula plana*," *Biol. Bull.* 97:239-240.

Hall, J.R. 1973. "Intraspecific trail-following in the marsh periwinkle *Littorina irrorata* Say," *Veliger* 16:72-75.

Hausman, S.A. 1932. "A contribution to the ecology of the salt marsh snail, *Melampus bidentatus* Say," *Amer. Nat.* 6:541-545.

Hausman, S.A. 1936. "Food and feeding activities of the salt marsh snail (*Melampus bidentatus*)," *Anat. Rec.* 67:127.

Hopkins, S.H. 1956. "*Odostomia impressa* parasitizing southern oysters," *Science* 124:628-629.

Hurst, A. 1965. "The feeding habits of *Nassarius vibex* (Say)," Proc. Malac. Soc. Lond. 36:313-317.

Johnson, J.K. 1972. "Effect of turbidity on the rate of filtration and growth of the slipper limpet, *Crepidula fornicata* Lamarck, 1799," *Veliger* 14:315-320.

Kornicker, L.S. 1961. "Observations on the behavior of the littoral gastropod *Terebra salleana*," *Ecology* 42:207.

Magalhaes, H. 1948. "An ecological study of snails of the genus *Busycon* at Beaufort, North Carolina," *Ecol. Monogr.* 18:377-409.

Marcus, E., and E. Marcus. 1960. "Some opisthobranchs from the northwestern Gulf of Mexico," *Publ. Inst. Mar. Sci. Texas* 6:251-264.

Mollick, R.S. 1973. "Some aspects of the biology of *Terebra dislocata* Say, 1822 (Gastropoda: Prosobranchia)," *Veliger* 16:82-84.

Olsson, A.A., and L.E. Crovo. 1968. "Observations on aquarium specimens of *Oliva sayana* Ravenal," *Veliger* 11:31-32.

Russell-Hunter, W.D., M.L. Apley, and R.D. Hunter. 1972. "Early life-history of *Melampus* and the significance of semilunar synchrony," *Biol. Bull.* 143:623-656.

Strenth, N.E., and J.E. Blankenship. 1978. "On the valid name of the common Texas and Florida species of *Aplysia* (Gastropoda, Ophistobranchia)." *Bull. Mar. Sci.* 28:249-254.

Tunnell, J.W., Jr. 1969. "The mollusks of Seven and One-Half Fathom Reef." M.S. Thesis, Texas A&I Univ. 83 p.

Voss, N.A. 1959. "Studies on the pulmonate gastropod *Siphonaria pectinata* (Linnaeus) from the southeast coast of Florida," *Bull. Mar. Sci.* 9:84-99.

Wells, H.W. 1958a. "Predation of pelecypods and gastropods by *Fasciolaria hunteria* (Perry)," *Bull. Mar. Sci.* 8:152-166.

Wells, H.W. 1958b. "The feeding habits of *Murex fulvescens*," *Ecology* 39:556-558.

Wells, H.W. 1959. "Notes on *Odostomia impressa* (Say)," *Nautilus* 72:140-144.

Wilson, D.P., and M.A. Wilson, 1956. "A contribution to the biology of *Ianthina janthina* (L.)," *J. Mar. Biol. Assoc.* U.K. 35:291-305.

Zischke, J.A. 1974. "Spawning, development and growth in the pulmonate limpets *Siphonaria pectinata* Linnaeus, 1758, and *Siphonaria alternata* Say, 1822," *Veliger* 16:399-404.

Pelecypoda

Ansell, A.D. 1968. "The rate of growth of the hard clam *Mercenaria mercenaria* (L.) throughout the geographical range," *J. Cons. Perm. Int. Explor. Mer.* 31:364-409.

Baugham, J.L., and B.B. Baker. 1951. "Oysters in Texas," *Texas Game, Fish and Oyster Comm. Bull.* 29:1-37.

Carriker, M.R. 1961. "Interrelation of functional morphology, behavior, and autecology in early stages of the bivalve *Mercenaria mercenaria*," *J. Elisha Mitchell Sci. Soc.* 77:168-241.

Cary, L.R. 1907. "The cultivation of oysters in Louisiana," *Bull. Gulf Biol. Sta.* 8:1-56.

Chanely, P. 1965. "Larval development of the brackish water mactrid clam, *Rangia cuneata*," *Chesapeake Sci.* 6:209-213.

D'Asaro, C.N. 1967. "The morphology of larval and postlarval *Chione cancellata* Linne (Eulamellibranchia: Veneridae) reared in the laboratory," *Bull. Mar. Sci.* 17:949-972.

Davis, H.C. 1953. "On food and feeding of larvae of the American oyster, *C. virginica*," *Biol. Bull.* 104:334-350.

Fairbanks, L.D. 1963. "Biodemographic studies of the clam *Rangia cuneata* Gray," *Tulane Stud. Zool.* 10:3-47.

Fraser, T.H. 1967. "Contributions to the biology of *Tagelus divisus* (Tellinacea: Pelecypoda) in Biscayne Bay, Florida," *Bull. Mar. Sci.* 17:111-132.

Gillard, R.M. 1969. "An ecological study of an oyster population, including selected associated organisms in West Bay, Galveston, Texas," M.Sc. Thesis. Texas A&M Univ.

Gunter, G. 1951. "The species of oysters of the Gulf, Caribbean and West Indian region," *Bull. Mar. Sci.* 1:40-45.

Gutsell, J.S. 1930. "Natural history of the bay scallop," *Bull. U.S. Bur. Fish.* 46:569-632.

Kane, H.E. 1961. "Occurrence of *Rangia cuneata* Gray and *Crassostrea virginica* (Gmelin) in Sabine Lake, Texas-Louisiana," *J. Sediment. Petrol.* 31:627.

Kuenzler, E.S. 1961. "Structure and energy flow of a mussel population in a Georgia salt marsh," *Limnol. Oceanogr.* 6:191-204.

Lent, C.M. 1969. "Adaptations of the ribbed mussel, *Modiolus demissus* (Dillwyn), to the intertidal habitat," *Amer. Zool.* 9:283-292.

Loesch, H.C. 1957. "Studies of the ecology of two species of *Donax* on Mustang Island, Texas," *Publ. Inst. Mar. Sci. Texas* 4:201-227.

Loesch, J.G. and D.S. Haven. 1973. "Estimated growth functions and size-age relationships of the hard clam, *Mercenaria mercenaria*, in the York River, Virginia," *Veliger* 16:76-81.

Loosanoff, V.L. 1966. "Time and intensity of settling of the oyster *Crassostrea virginica*, in Long Island Sound," *Biol. Bull.* 130:211-227.

Menzel, R.W., and F.E. Nichy. 1958. "Studies of the distribution and feeding habits of some oyster predators in Alligator Harbor, Florida," *Bull. Mar. Sci.* 8:125-145.

Moore, H.B., and N.N. Lopez. 1969. "The ecology of *Chione cancellata*," *Bull. Mar. Sci.* 19:131-148.

O'Heeron, M.K. 1966. "Some aspects of the ecology of *Rangia cuneata* (Gray)," M. Sc. Thesis. Texas A&M Univ.

Tiffany, W.J., III. 1971. "The tidal migration of *Donax variabilis* Say," *Veliger* 14:82-85.

Trussell, P.C. 1967. "Teredine borers," *Sea Frontiers* 13:234-243.

Tunnell, J.W., Jr., and A.H. Chaney. 1970. "A checklist of the mollusks of Seven and One-Half Fathom Reef, northwestern Gulf of Mexico." *Contrib. Mar. Sci.* 15:193-203.

Turner, H.J., Jr., and D.L. Belding. 1957. "The tidal migrations of *Donax variabilis* Say," *Limnol. Oceanogr.* 2:120-124.

Turner, R.D. 1954. "The family Pholadidae in the western Atlantic and eastern Pacific, Part. I, Pholadinae," *Johnsonia* 3:1-63.

Turner, R.D., and J. Rosewater. 1958. "The family Pinnidae in the western Atlantic," *Johnsonia* 3:285-328.

Wardle, W.J. 1970. "Contributions to the biology of *Tagelus plebius* (Bivalvia: Tellinacea) in Galveston Bay, Texas," M. Sc. Thesis. Texas A&M Univ.

Wells, H.W., M.J. Wells, and I.E. Gray. 1964. "The calico scallop community in North Carolina," *Bull. Mar. Sci.* 14:561-593.

Wolfe, D.A., and E.N. Petteway. 1968. "Growth of *Rangia cuneata*," *Chesapeake Sci.* 9:99-102.

Scaphopoda

Gainey, L.F., Jr. 1972. "The use of the foot and the captacula in the feeding of *Dentalium* (Mollusca: Scaphopoda)," *Veliger* 15:29-34.

Cephalopoda

Arnold, J.M. 1962. "Mating behavior and social structure in *Loligo pealei*," *Biol. Bull.* 123:53-57.

Dillon, L.S., and R.O. Dial. 1962. "Notes on the morphology of the common Gulf squid *Lolliguncula brevis* (Blainville)," *Texas J. Sci.* 14:156-166.

Harry, H.W., and S.F. Snider. 1969. "Cuttlebones on the beach at Galveston," *Veliger* 12:89-94.

Kelly, J.A., Jr., and A. Dragovich. 1967. "Occurrence of the squid, *Lolliguncula brevis*, in some coastal waters of western Florida," *Bull. Mar. Sci.* 17:840-883.

Lipka, D.A. 1975. "The systematics and zoogeography of cephalopods from the Gulf of Mexico." Ph.D. Diss., Texas A&M Univ. 347 p.

Voss, G.L. 1954. "Cephalopoda of the Gulf of Mexico," *U.S. Fish Wildl. Serv. Fish. Bull.* 55:475-478.

Voss, G.L. 1956. "A review of the cephalopods of the Gulf of Mexico," *Bull. Mar. Sci.* 6:85-178.

Cirripedia

Causey, D. 1961. "The barnacle genus *Octolasmis* in the Gulf of Mexico," *Turtox News* 39:51-55.

Causey, D. 1962. "The ivory barnacle," *Turtox News* 40:178-183.

Darwin, C. 1851. "A monograph on the subclass Cirripedia, with figures of all species. The Lepadidae; or, pedunculated cirripedes," Ray Soc., Lond.

Darwin, C. 1854. "A monograph on the subclass Cirripedia, with figures of all species. The Balanidae, (or sessile cirripedes); the Verrucidae, etc., etc., etc.," Ray Soc., Lond.

Dawson, C.E. 1957. "*Balanus* fouling of shrimp," *Science* 126:1068.

Doochin, H.D. 1951. "The morphology of *Balanus improvisus* Darwin and *Balanus amphitrite niveus* Darwin during initial attachment and metamorphosis," *Bull. Mar. Sci.* 1:15-39.

Eldred, B. 1962. "The attachment of the barnacle, *Balanus amphitrite niveus* Darwin, and other fouling organisms to the rock shrimp, *Sicyonia dorsalis* Kingsley," *Crustaceana* 3:203-206.

Gordon, C.M. 1969. "The apparent influence of salinity on the distribution of barnacle species in Chesapeake Bay (Cirripedia)," *Crustaceana* 16:139-142.

Hulings, N.C. 1961. "The barnacles and decapod fauna from the nearshore area of Panama City, Florida," *Quart. J. Fla. Acad. Sci.* 24:215-222.

Jones, E.C. 1968. "*Lepas anserifera* Linne (Cirripedia: Lepodomorpha) feeding on fish and *Physalia*," *Crustaceana* 14:312-313.

Lang, W.H. 1976. "The larval development and metamorphosis of the pedunculate barnacle *Octolasmis mulleri* (Coker, 1902) reared in the laboratory." *Biol. Bull.* 150.255-267.

Moore, H.B., and A.C. Frue, 1959. "The settlement and growth of *Balanus improvisus, B. eburneus* and *B. amphitrite* in the Miami area," *Bull. Mar. Sci.* 9:421-440.

Pilsbry, H.A. 1916. "The sessile barnacles (Cirripedia) contained in the collections of the U.S. National Museum, including a monograph of the American species," *Bull. U.S. Natn. Mus.* 93:1-366.

Thomas, P.J. 1975. "The fouling community on selected oil platforms off Louisiana, with special emphasis on the Cirripedia fauna." M.S. Thesis, Fla. St. Univ. vi + 129 p.

Amphipoda

Bousfield, E.L. 1973. *Shallow-water gammaridean amphipoda of New England.* Cornell Univ. Press.

Dougherty, E.C., and J.E. Steinberg. 1953. "Notes on the skeleton shrimps (Crustacea: Caprellidae) of California," *Proc. Biol. Soc. Wash.* 66:39-50.

Keith, D.E. 1969. "Aspects of feeding in *Caprella californica* Stimpson and *Caprella equilibra* Say (Amphipoda)," *Crustaceana* 16:119-124.

McCain, J.C. 1965. "The Caprellidae (Crustacea: Amphipoda) of Virginia," *Chesapeake Sci.* 6:190-196.

McCain, J.C. 1968. "The Caprellidae (Crustacea: Amphipoda) of the western North Atlantic," *Bull. U S. Natn. Mus.* 278:1-147.

McKinney, L.D. 1977. "The origin and distribution of shallow water gammaridean Amphipoda in the Gulf of Mexico and Caribbean Sea with notes on their ecology." Ph.D. Diss., Texas A&M Univ. xviii + 401 p.

Shoemaker, C.R. 1947. "Further notes on the amphipod genus *Corophium* from the east coast of America," *J. Wash. Acad. Sci.* 37:47-63.

Steinberg, J.E., and E.C. Dougherty. 1957. "The skeleton shrimps (Crustacea: Caprellidae) of the Gulf of Mexico," *Tulane Stud. Zool.* 5:265-288.

Isopoda

Markham, J.C. 1978. "Bopyrid isopods parasitizing hermit crabs in the northwestern Atlantic Ocean." *Bull. Mar. Sci.* 28:102-117.

Menzies, R.J. 1951 (1954). "A new subspecies of marine isopod from Texas," Proc. U.S. Natn. Mus. 101:575-579.

Menzies, R.J. 1957. "The marine borer family Limnoriidae (Crustacea; Isopoda)," *Bull. Mar. Sci.* 7:101-200.

Menzies, R.J., and D. Frankenberg. 1966. "Handbook of the common marine isopod Crustacea of Georgia," Univ. of Ga. Press.

Menzies, R.J., and M.A. Miller. 1955. "A redescription of the marine isopod crustacean *"Exosphaeroma" faxoni* Richardson from Texas," *Bull. Mar. Sci.* 5:292-296.

Miller, M.A. 1968. "Isopoda and Tanaidacea from buoys in coastal waters of the continental United States, Hawaii, and the Bahamas (Crustacea)," *Proc. U.S. Natn. Mus.* 125:1-53.

Rehm, A., and H.J. Humm. 1973. "*Sphaeroma terebrans:* A threat to the mangroves of southwestern Florida," *Science* 182:173-174.

Reish, D.J., and W.M. Hetherington. 1969. "The effects of hyper- and hypochlorinities on members of the wood-boring genus *Limnoria*," *Mar. Biol.* 2:137-139.

Richardson, H. 1905. "A monograph on the isopods of North America," *Bull. U.S. Natn. Mus.* 54:1-727.

Schafer, R.D., and C.E. Lane. 1957. "Some preliminary observations bearing on the nutrition of *Limnoria*," *Bull. Mar. Sci.* 7:289-296.

Decapoda

Anderson, W.W., and M.J. Lindner. 1945. "A provisional key to the shrimps of the family Penaeidae with especial reference to American forms," *Trans. Amer. Fish. Soc.* 73:284-319.

Anderson, W.W., J.E. King, and M.J. Lindner. 1949. "Early stages in the life history of the common marine shrimp, *Penaeus setiferus* (Linnaeus)," *Biol. Bull.* 97:168-172.

Ayers, J.C. 1938. "Relationship of habitat to oxygen consumption by certain estuarine crabs," *Ecology* 19:523-527.

Baxter, K.N., and W.C. Renfro. 1967. "Seasonal occurrence and size distribution of postlarval brown and white shrimp near Galveston, Texas, with notes on species identification," *U.S. Fish Wildl. Serv. Fish. Bull.* 66:149-158.

Behre, E.H. 1954. "Decapoda of the Gulf of Mexico," *U.S. Fish Wildl. Serv. Fish. Bull.* 55:451-455.

Bishop, J.M., and W.F. Herrnkind. 1976. "Burying and molting of pink shrimp, *Penaeus duorarum (Crustacea: Penaeidae), under selected photoperiods of white light and UV-light." Biol. Bull.* 150:163-182.

Bliss, D.E. 1968. "Transition from water to land in decapod crustaceans," *Amer. Zool.* 8:355-392.

Borradaile, L.A. 1915. "On the species of *Lucifer* and their distribution," *Ann. Mag. Nat. Hist.,* Ser. 8, 16:226-231.

Brown, F.A., Jr., and G.C. Stephens. 1951. "Studies of the daily rhythmicity of the fiddler crab, *Uca*," Modifications by photoperiod, *Biol. Bull.* 101:71-83.

Burkenroad, M.D. 1934. "The Penaeidea of Louisiana with a discussion of their world relationships," *Bull. Amer. Mus. Nat. Hist.* 68:61-143.

Christensen, A.M., and J.J. McDermott. 1958. "Life-history and biology of the oyster crab, *Pinnotheres ostreum* Say," *Biol. Bull.* 114:146-179.

Compton, H. 1965. "A study of Texas shrimp populations; biological survey of the commercial shrimp and associated organisms in the inshore Gulf of Mexico," Texas Parks Wildl. Dept., Coastal Fish Proj. Rept. 1964, Proj. No. MS-R-6:145-147.

Conte, F.S. 1971. "Ecological aspects of selected crustacea of two marsh embayments on the Texas coast," Ph.D. Diss., Texas A&M Univ.

Cook, H.L. 1965. "A generic key to the protozoean, mysis, and postlarval stages of the littoral Penaeidae of the northwestern Gulf of Mexico," *U.S. Fish Wildl. Serv. Fish. Bull.* 65:437-447.

Cook, H.L., and M.A. Murphy. 1965. "Early developmental stages of the rock shrimp, *Sicyonia brevirostris* Stimpson, reared in the laboratory," *Tulane Stud. Zool.* 12:109-127.

Costlow, J.D., Jr., and C.G. Bookhout. 1960. "The complete larval development of *Sesarma cinereum* (Bosc) reared in the laboratory," *Biol. Bull.* 118:203-214.

Costlow, J.D., Jr., and C.G. Bookhout. 1962. "The larval development of *Sesarma reticulatum* Say reared in the laboratory," *Crustaceana* 4:281-294.

Crane, J. 1957. "Basic patterns of display in fiddler crabs (Ocypodidae: Genus *Uca*)," *Zoologica* 42:69-82.

Cummings, W.C. 1961. "Maturation and spawning of the pink shrimp, *Penaeus duorarum* Burkenroad," *Trans. Amer. Fish. Soc.* 90:462-468.

Darnell, R.M. 1959. "Studies of the life history of the blue crab (*Callinectes sapidus* Rathbun) in Louisiana waters," *Trans. Amer. Fish. Soc.* 88:294-304.

Dobkin, S. 1961. "Early development stages of the pink shrimp, *Penaeus duorarum*, from Florida waters," *U.S. Fish Wildl. Serv. Fish. Bull.* 61:321-349.

Efford, I.E. 1967. "The antennule cleaning setae in the sand crab, *Emerita* (Decapoda, Hippidae)," *Crustaceana* 21:316-318.

Eisler, R. 1969. Acute toxicities of insecticides to marine decapod crustaceans," *Crustaceana* 16:302-310.

Felder, D.L. 1971. "The decapod crustaceans of Seven and One-Half Fathom Reef." M.S. Thesis, Texas A&I Univ. 103 p.

Felder, D.L. 1973. "An annotated key to crabs and lobsters (Decapoda, Reptantia) from coastal waters of the northwestern Gulf of Mexico," Louisiana St. Univ., Sea Grant Publ. No. LSU-SG-73-02.

Fingerman, M.R. 1957. "Relation between position of burrows and tidal rhythm of *Uca*," *Biol. Bull.* 112:7-20.

Fingerman, M.R., R. Nagabhushanam, and L. Philpott. 1961. "Physiology of the melanophores of the crab *Sesarma reticulatum*," *Biol. Bull.* 120:337-347.

Gifford, C.A. 1963. "Some observations on the general biology of the land crab, *Cardisoma guanhumi* (Latreille) in South Florida," *Biol. Bull.* 123:207-223.

Goodbody, I. 1965. "Continuous breeding in populations of two tropical crustaceans *Mysidium columbiae* (Zimmer) and *Emerita portoricensis* (Schmitt)," *Ecology* 46:195-197.

Gordon, J. 1956. "A bibliography of pagurid crabs, exclusive of Alcock, 1905," *Bull. Amer. Mus. Nat. Hist.* 108:255-352.

Gray, I.E. 1957. "A comparative study of the gill area of crabs," *Biol. Bull.* 112:34-42.

Haig, J. 1956. "The Galatheidae (Crustacea: Anomura) of the Allan Hancock Expedition with a review of the Porcellanidae of the western Atlantic," *Allan Hancock Atlantic Exp., Rept.* 8:1-44.

Haley, S.R. 1969. "Relative growth and sexual maturity of the Texas ghost crab, *Ocypode quadrata*," *Crustaceana* 17:285-297.

Haley, S.R. 1972. "Reproductive cycling in the ghost crab, *Ocypode quadrata*," *Crustaceana* 23:1-11.

Harper, D.E., Jr. 1968. "Distribution of *Lucifer faxoni* (Crustacea: Decapoda: Sergestidae) in neritic waters off the Texas coast, with a note on the occurrence of *Lucifer typus*," *Contri. Mar. Sci.*, Univ. Texas Mar. Sci. Inst. 13:1-16.

Hazlett, B. 1962. "Aspects of the biology of the snapping shrimp (*Alpheus* and *Synalpheus*)," *Crustaceana* 4:82-83.

Herreid, C.F. 1969. "Integument permeability of crabs and adaptation to land." *Comp. Biochem. Physiol.* 29:423-429.

Herreid. C.F., and C.A. Gifford. 1963. "The burrow habitat of the land crab *Cardisoma guanhumi* (Latreille)," *Ecology* 44:773-775.

Hinsch, G.W. 1972. "Some factors controlling reproduction in the spider crab, *Libinia emarginata*," *Biol. Bull.* 143:358-366.

Holland, C.A., and D.M. Skinner. 1976. "Interactions between molting and regeneration in the land crab." *Biol. Bull.* 150:222-240.

Hughes, D.A. 1969. "Responses to salinity change as a tidal transport mechanism of pink shrimp, *Penaeus duorarum*," *Biol. Bull.* 136:43-53.

Jensen, J.P. 1958. "The relation between body size and number of eggs in marine Malacostraca," *Meddr. Danm. Fisk.-og Havunders* 2:1-28.

Johnson, L.C. 1940. "The correlation of water movements and dispersal of pelagic littoral animals, especially the sand crab, *Emerita*," *J. Mar. Res.* 2:236-245.

Johnson, M.W., F.A. Everest, and R.W. Young. 1947. "The role of snapping shrimp (*Crangon* and *Synalpheus*) in the production of underwater noise in the sea," *Biol. Bull.* 93:122-138.

Kinne, O., E.K. Shirley and H.E. Meen. 1963. "Osmotic responses of hermit crabs (Pagurus longicarpus Say) exposed to various constant temperatures and salinities," *Crustaceana* 5:317.

Landers, W.S. 1954. "Notes on the predation of the hard clam, *Venus mercenaria*, by the mud crab, *Neopanope texana*," *Ecology* 35:422.

Laughlin, R.B., Jr., L.G.L. Young, and J.M. Neff. 1978. "A long-term study of the effects of water-soluble fractions of No. 2 fuel oil on the sur-vival, development rate, and growth of the mud crab, *Rhithropanopeus harrisii*." *Mar. Biol.* 47:87-95.

Limbaugh, C., H. Pederson, and F.A. Chace, Jr. 1961. "Shrimps that clean fishes," *Bull. Mar. Sci.* 11:237-257.

Lunz, G.R. 1947. *"Callinectes versus Ostrea,"* *J. Elisha Mitchell Sci. Soc.* 63:81.

MacGinitie, G.E. 1937. "Notes on the natural history of several marine Crustacea," *Amer. Midl. Nat.* 18:1031-1036.

Menzel, R.W. 1955. "Crabs as predators of oysters in Louisiana," Proc. Natn. Shellfish. Assoc. 46:177-184.

Miller, D.C. 1961. "The feeding mechanism of fiddler crabs, with ecological considerations of feeding adaptations," *Zoologica* 46:89-100.

Moffett, A.W. 1967. "The shrimp fishery in Texas," *Texas Parks Wildl. Dept. Bull.* 50:1-36.

Overstreet, R.M. 1973. "Parasites of some penaeid shrimps with emphasis on reared hosts." *Aquaculture* 2:105-140.

Parker, J.C. 1966. "A study of the distribution and condition of brown shrimp in the primary nursery areas of the Galveston Bay System, Texas," M. Sc. Thesis. Texas A&M Univ.

Pautsch, F., L. Lawinski, and K. Turboboyski. 1969. "Zur ökologie der Krabbe *Rithropanopeus harrisii* (Gould) (Xanthidae)," *Limnologica,* Berlin 7:63-68.

Pearse, A.S. 1945. "Ecology of *Upogebia affinis* (Say)," *Ecology* 26:303-305.

Porter, H.J. 1960. "Zoeal stages of the stone crab, *Menippe mercenaria* Say," *Chesapeake Sci.* 1:168-177.

Powell, E.H., Jr., and G. Gunter. 1968. "Observations on the stone crab, *Menippe mercenaria* Say, in the vicinity of Port Aransas, Texas," *Gulf Res. Rept.* 2:285-299.

Powers, L.W. 1977. "A catalogue and bibliography to the crabs (Brachyura) of the Gulf of Mexico." *Contri. Mar. Sci.* 20 (Supp.):1-190.

Provenzano, A.J. 1959. "The shallow-water hermit crabs of Florida," *Bull. Mar. Sci.* 9:349-420.

Pullen, E.J., and W.L. Trent. 1969. "White shrimp emigration in relation to size, sex, temperature and salinity," *F.A.O. Fish. Rept.* No. 57:1001-1014.

Rathbun, M.J. 1918. "The grapsoid crabs of America," *U.S. Natn. Mus. Bull.* 97:1-461.

Rathbun, M.J. 1925. "The spider crabs of America," *U.S. Natn. Mus. Bull.* 129:1-612.

Rathbun, M.J. 1930. "The cancroid crabs of America of the families Euryhalidae, Portunidae, Atelecyclidae, Cancridae and Xanthidae," *U.S. Natn. Mus. Bull.* 152:1-609.

Ray, C. 1967. "*Gecarcinus lateralis* Freminville in Texas," *Texas J. Sci.* 19:109.

Ray, J.P. 1974. "A study of the coral reef crustaceans (Decapoda and Stomatopoda) of two Gulf of Mexico reef systems: West Flower Garden, Texas, and Isla de Lobos, Veracruz, Mexico." Ph.D. Diss., Texas A&M Univ., xxxi + 323 p.

Rebach, S. 1969. "Seasonal migrations of the hermit crab, *Pagurus longicarpus*," *Amer. Zool.* 9:1075.

Rebach, S. 1974. "Burying behavior in relation to substrate and temperature in the hermit crab, *Pagurus longicarpus*," *Ecology* 55:195-198.

Roberts, M.H., Jr. 1968. "Functional morphology of mouthparts of the hermit crabs, *Pagurus longicarpus* and *Pagurus pollicaris*." *Chesapeake Sci.* 9:9-20.

Ryan, E.P. 1956. "Observations on the life histories and the distribution of the Xanthidae (mud crabs) of Chesapeake Bay," *Amer. Midl. Nat.* 56:138-162.

Sandoz, M., and S.H. Hopkins. 1947. "Early life history of the oyster crab, *Pinnotheres ostreum* (Say)," *Biol. Bull.* 93:250-258.

Savage, T. 1971. "Mating of the stone crab, *Menippe mercenaria* (Say) (Decapoda, Brachyura)," *Crustaceana* 20:315-316.

Shoup, J.B. 1968. "Shell opening by crabs of the genus *Calappa*," *Science* 160:887-888.

Stauber, L.A. 1945. "*Pinnotheres ostreum*, parasitic on the American oyster, *Ostrea* (Gryphaea) *virginica*," *Biol. Bull.* 88:269-291.

Tashian, R.E., and F.J. Vernberg. 1958. "The specific distinctness of the fiddler crabs *Uca pugnax* (Smith) and *Uca rapax* (Smith) at their zone of overlap in northeastern Florida," *Zoologica* 43:89-91.

Teal, J.M. 1958. "Distribution of fiddler crabs in Georgia salt marshes," *Ecology* 39:185-193.

Teal, J.M., and F.G. Carey. 1959. "The metabolism of marsh crabs under conditions of reduced pressure," *Physiol. Zool.* 40:83-91.

Voss, G.L. 1956. "Protective coloration and habitat of the shrimp *Tozeuma carolinensis* Kingsley (Caridea: Hippolytidae)," *Bull. Mar. Sci.* 6:359-363.

Wass, M.L. 1955. "The decapod crustaceans of Alligator Harbor and adjacent inshore areas of northwestern Florida," *Quart. J. Fla. Acad. Sci.* 18:129-176.

Wear, R.G. 1970. "Notes and bibliography on the larvae of xanthid crabs," *Pac. Sci.* 24:84-89.

Wickham, D.A., and F.C. Minkler, III. 1975. "Laboratory observations on daily patterns of burrowing and locomotor activity of pink shrimp, *Penaeus duorarum,* brown shrimp, *Penaeus aztecus,* and white shrimp, *Penaeus setiferus.*" *Contrib. Mar. Sci.* 19:21-35.

Wilkins, J.G. 1975. "Contributions to the biology and ecology of *Petrolisthes armatus* (Anomura, Porcellanidae)." M.S. Thesis, Texas A&M Univ. 58 p.

Williams, A.B. 1958. "Substrates as a factor in shrimp distribution," *Limnol. Oceanogr.* 3:283-290.

Williams, A.B. 1965. "Marine decapod crustaceans of the Carolinas," *U.S. Fish Wildl. Serv. Fish. Bull.* 65:1-298.

Wilson, E.B. 1903. "Notes on the reversal of asymmetry in the regeneration of the chelae in *Alpheus heterochaelis,*" *Biol. Bull.* 4:197-210.

Wolcott, T.G. 1978. "Ecological role of ghost crabs, *Ocypode quadrata* (Fabricius) on an ocean beach: scavengers or predators." *J. Exp. Mar. Biol. Ecol.* 31:67-82.

Wood, C.E. 1967. "Physioecology of the grass shrimp, *Palaemonetes pugio,* in the Galveston Bay Estuarine System," *Contr. Mar. Sci.,* Inst. Mar. Sci. Texas 12:54-79.

Other Crustacea

Bowman, T.E. 1964. "*Mysidopsis almyra,* a new estuarine mysid crustacean from Louisiana and Florida," *Tulane Stud. Zool.* 12:15-18.

Hedgpeth, J.W. 1948 (1950). "The Pycnogonida of the western North Atlantic and Caribbean," *Proc. U.S. Natn. Mus.* 97:157-342.

Ives, J.E. 1891. "Crustacea from the northern coast of Yucatan, the harbor of Vera Cruz, the west coast of Florida and the Bermuda Islands," *Proc. Acad. Nat. Sci. Phila.* 43:176-207.

Molenock, J. 1969. "*Mysidopsis bahia,* a new species of mysid (Crustacea: Mysidacea) from Galveston Bay, Texas," *Tulane Stud. Zool. Bot.* 15:113-116.

Parks, H.B. 1940. "Descriptive catalogue of the crustacea of the Gulf coast of Texas," *Tech. Bull. Stephen F. Austin St. Teachers Coll.* 2:1-5.

Pearse, A.S. 1952. "Parasitic crustacea from the Texas coast," *Publ. Inst. Mar. Sci. Texas* 2:5-42.

Price, W.W. 1976. "The abundance and distribution of Mysidacea in the shallow waters of Galveston Island, Texas." Ph.D. Diss., Texas A&M Univ. xvi + 207 p.

Reinhard, E.G. 1950. "The morphology of *Loxothylacus texanus* Boschma, a sacculinid parasite of the blue crab," *Texas J. Sci.* 2:360-365.

Say, T. 1818. "An account of the Crustacea of the United States," *J. Acad. Nat. Sci. Phila.* 1:37-401.

Tattersall, W.M. 1951. "The Mysidacea of the United States National Museum," *Bull. U.S. Natn. Mus.* 201:1-292.

Bryozoa

Canu, F., and R.S. Bassler. 1928. "Fossil and recent Bryozoa of the Gulf of Mexico region," *Proc. U.S. Natn. Mus.* 72:1-199.

Lagaaij, R. 1963. "New additions to the bryozoan fauna of the Gulf of Mexico," *Publ. Inst. Mar. Sci. Texas* 9:162-236.

Maturo, F. 1957. "Bryozoa of Beaufort, North Carolina," *J. Elisha Mitchell Sci. Soc.* 73:11-68.

Osburn, R.C. 1954. "The Bryozoa of the Gulf of Mexico," *U.S. Fish Wildl. Serv. Fish. Bull.* 89:361-362.

Ryland, J.S. 1976. "Physiology and ecology of marine bryozoans." *Adv. Mar. Biol.* 14:285-443.

Echinodermata

Bell, B.M., and R.W. Frey. 1969. "Observations on ecology and the feeding and burrowing mechanisms of *Mellita quinquiesperforata* (Leske)," *J. Paleont.* 43:553-560.

Burke, T.E. 1974. "Echinodermata of the West Flower Garden Reef Bank," M.S. Thesis, Texas A&M Univ. 165 p.

Downey, M.E. 1973. "Starfishes from the Caribbean and the Gulf of Mexico." *Smithsonian Contrib. Zool.* 126:1-158.

Fell, H.B. 1966. "The ecology of ophiuroids." *In Physiology of Echinodermata.* R.A. Boolootian (Ed.). New York: Interscience.

Hyman, L.H. 1958. "Notes on the biology of the five-lunuled sand dollar," *Biol. Bull.* 114:54-56.

Moore D.R. 1956. "Observations of predation on echinoderms by three species of Cassidae," *Nautilus* 69:73-76.

Gray, I.E., M.E. Downey, and M.J. Cerame-Vivas. 1968. "Sea-stars of North Carolina," *U.S. Fish Wildl. Serv. Fish. Bull.* 67:127-163.

Shirley, T.C. 1973. "The echinoderms of Seven and One-Half Fathom Reef." M.S. Thesis, Texas A&I Univ. 82 p.

Thomas, L.P. 1965. "A new species of *Ophiophragmus* (Ophiuroidea, Echinodermata) from the Gulf of Mexico." *Bull. Mar. Sci.* 15:850-854.

Weihe, S.C., and I.E. Gray. 1968. "Observations on the biology of the sand dollar *Mellita quinquiesperforata* (Leske)," *J. Elisha Mitchell Sci. Soc.* 84:315:327.

Wells, H.W., M.J. Wells, and I.E. Gray. 1961. "Food of the sea-star *Astropecten articulatus,*" *Biol. Bull.* 120:265-271.

Chaetognatha

Adelmann, H.C. 1967. "The taxonomy and summer and fall vertical distribution of the chaetognatha off Galveston, Texas," Ph. D. Diss. Texas A&M Univ.

Pierce, E.L. 1951. "The chaetognatha of the west coast of Florida," *Biol. Bull.* 100:206-228.

Pierce, E.L. 1962. "Chaetognatha from the Texas coast," *Publ. Inst. Mar. Sci. Texas* 8:147-152.

Reeve, M.R. 1964. "Feeding of zooplankton, with special reference to some experiments with *Sagitta,*" *Nature,* Lond. 201:211-213.

Tokioka, T. 1955. "Notes on some chaetognaths from the Gulf of Mexico," *Bull. Mar. Sci.* 5:52-65.

Chordata

Cory, R.L., and E.L. Pierce. 1967. "Distribution and ecology of lancelots (order Amphioxi) over the continental shelf of the southeastern United States." *Limnol. Oceanogr.* 12:650-656.

Fenaux, R. 1966. "Synonymie et distribution géographique des Appendiculaires," *Bull. Inst. Oceanogr. Monaco* 66:1-23.

Van Name, W.G. 1945. "The North and South American ascidians," *Bull. Amer. Mus. Nat. Hist.* 84:1-476.

Miscellaneous Taxa

Chitwood, B.G. 1951a. "A marine tardigrade from the Gulf of Mexico," *Texas J. Sci.* 3:111-112.

Chitwood, B.G. 1951b. "North American marine nematodes," *Texas J. Sci.* 3:617-672.

Coe, W.R. 1951. "The nemertean faunas of the Gulf of Mexico and of southern Florida," *Bull. Mar. Sci.* 1:149-186.

Fisher, W.K. 1947 (1950). "New genera and species of echiuroid and sipunculoid worms," *Proc. U.S. Natn. Mus.* 97:351-372.

Gerauld, J.H. 1913. "The sipunculids of the eastern coast of North America," *Proc. U.S. Natn. Mus.* 44:373-437.

Henry, C.A. 1976. "The commensal clam, *Paramya subovata* (Bivalvia:Myidae) and *Thalassema hartmani* (Echiuroidea) off Galveston, Texas." *Nautilus* 90:73-74.

Hopper, B.E. 1961. "Marine nematodes from the coast line of the Gulf of Mexico," *Canad. J. Zool.* 39:183-199.

Long, C.D. 1960. "A phoronid from the Gulf of Mexico," *Bull. Mar. Sci.* 10:204-207.

Paine, R.T. 1961. "Observations on *Phoronis architecta* in Florida waters." *Bull. Mar. Sci.* 11:457-462.

Paine, R.T. 1963. "Ecology of the brachiopod *Glottidia pyramidata."* *Ecol. Monogr.* 33:187-213.

Short, R.B. 1962. "Two new dicyemid mesozoans from the Gulf of Mexico," *Tulane Stud. Zool.* 9:101-111.

Willis, H.L. 1968. "Artificial key to the species of *Cicindela* of North America, north of Mexico (Coleoptera: Cicindelidae)," *J. Kans. Ent. Soc.* 41:303-317.

General References

Abbott, R.E. 1975. "The faunal composition of the algal-sponge zone of the Flower Garden Banks, northwest Gulf of Mexico." M.S. Thesis, Texas A&M Univ., 205 p.

Adams, J.A. 1960. A contribution to the biology and postlarval development of the Sargassum fish, *Histrio histrio* (Linnaeus), with a discussion of the *Sargassum* complex," *Bull. Mar. Sci.* 10:55-82.

Behre, E.H. 1950. "Annotated list of the fauna of the Grand Isle Region, 1928-1946," *Occ. Pap. Mar. Lab. La. St. Univ.* 6:1-66.

Bird, S.O. 1970. "Shallow-marine and estuarine benthic molluscan communities from the area of Beaufort, North Carolina," *Bull. Amer. Assoc. Petrol. Geol.* 54:1651-1676.

Breuer, J.P. 1957. "Ecological survey of Baffin and Alazan Bays, Texas," *Publ. Inst. Mar. Sci. Texas* 4:134-155.

Breuer, J.P. 1962. "An ecological survey of the lower Laguna Madre of Texas, 1953-1959," *Publ. Inst. Mar. Sci. Texas* 8:153-183.

Bright, T.J., and R. Rezak. 1976. "A biological and geological reconnaissance of selected topographic features on the Texas continental shelf. A final report to the U.S. Dept. of the Interior, Bureau of Land Management Outer Continental Shelf Office, New Orleans, Louisiana," Contract No. AA550-CT5-4. Texas A&M University Research Foundation and Texas A&M University Dept. of Oceanography.

Cary, L.R. 1906. "A contribution to the fauna of the coast of Louisiana," *Gulf Biol. Sta. Bull.* 6:50-59.

Chambers, G.V., and A.K. Sparks. 1959. "An ecological survey of the Houston Ship Channel and adjacent bays," *Publ. Inst. Mar. Sci.* 6:213-250.

Chandler, A.C. 1935. "Parasites of fishes in Galveston Bay," *Proc. U.S. Natn. Mus.* 83:123-155.

Connell, C.H., and J.B. Cross. 1950. "Mass mortality of fish associated with the protozoan *Gonyaulax* in the Gulf of Mexico," *Science* 112:359-363.

Copeland, B.J., and T.J. Bechtel. 1974. "Some environmental limits of six Gulf coast estuarine organisms." *Contrib. Mar. Sci.* 18:169-204.

Cross, J.C., and H.B. Parks, 1937. "Marine fauna and sea-side flora of the Nueces River basin and the adjacent islands," *Bull. Texas Coll. Arts & Indust.* 8:1-36.

Cuzon du Rest, R.P. 1962. "Distribution of the zooplankton in the salt marshes of southeastern Louisiana," M. Sc. Thesis. Texas A&M Univ.

Darnell, R.M. 1958. "Food habits of fishes and larger invertebrates of Lake Pontchartrain, Louisiana, an estuarine community," *Publ. Inst. Mar. Sci. Texas* 5:353-416.

Darnell, R.M. 1961. "Trophic spectrum of an estuarine community, based on studies of Lake Pontchartrain, Louisiana," *Ecology* 42:553-568.

David, P.M. 1965. "The surface fauna of the ocean," *Endeavour* 24:95-100.

Dawson, C.E. 1966. "Additions to the known marine fauna of Grand Isle, Louisiana," *Proc. La. Acad. Sci.* 29:175-180.

Defenbaugh, R.E. 1976. "A study of the benthic macroinvertebrates of the continental shelf of the northern Gulf of Mexico," Ph.D. Diss., Texas A&M Univ., 476 p.

Dooley, J.K. 1972. "Fishes associated with the pelagic Sargassum complex, with a discussion of the Sargassum community." *Contrib. Mar. Sci.* 16:1-32.

Frazer, R.D. 1921. "Early records of tropical hurricanes on the Texas coast in the vicinity of Galveston, Texas," *Monthly Weather Rev.* 49:454-457.

Gettleson, D.A. 1976. "An ecological study of the benthic meiofauna and macrofauna of a soft bottom area on the Texas outer continental shelf." Ph.D. Diss., Texas A&M Univ., xiv + 257 p.

Geyer, R.A. 1950. "A bibliography on the Gulf of Mexico," *Texas J. Sci.* 2:44-93.

Goodbody, I. 1961. "Mass mortality of a marine fauna following tropical rains," *Ecology* 42:150-155.

Gordon, M. 1938. "Animals of the Sargasso Sea merry-go-around. *Nat. Hist.,"* 42:12-20.

Gudger, E.W. 1937. "Sargassum weed fish "nests" made by flying fishes and not by Sargasso fish (Antennariidae): a historical review," *Amer. Nat.* 71:363-381.

Gunter, G. 1941. "Death of fishes due to cold on the Texas coast, January, 1940," *Ecology* 22:203-208.

Gunter, G. 1945. "Studies on marine fishes of Texas," *Publ. Inst. Mar. Sci. Texas* 1:1-190.

Gunter, G. 1950. "Seasonal population changes and distributions as related to salinity, of certain invertebrates of the Texas coast, including the commercial shrimp," *Publ. Inst. Mar. Sci. Texas* 1:7-51.

Gunter, G. 1952. "The import of catastrophic mortalities for marine fisheries along the Texas coast," *J. Wildl. Manag.* 16:63-69.

Gunter, G. 1956. "Some relations of faunal distributions to salinity in estuarine waters," *Ecology* 37:616-619.

Gunter, G. 1961. "Some relations of estuarine organisms to salinity," *Limnol. Oceanogr.* 6:182-190.

Gunter, G., and G.E. Hall. 1965. "A biological investigation of the Caloosahatchee Estuary of Florida," *Gulf Res. Rept.* 2:1-71.

Gunter, G., and H.H. Hildebrand. 1951. "Destruction of fishes and other organisms on the south Texas coast by the cold wave of January 28-February 3, 1951," *Ecology* 32:731-736.

Gunter, G., and R.A. Geyer. 1955. "Studies of fouling organisms of the northwest Gulf of Mexico," *Publ. Inst. Mar. Sci. Texas* 4:37-67.

Gunter, G., and W.E. Shell. 1958. "A study of an estuarine area with water-level control in the Louisiana marsh," *Proc. La. Acad. Sci.* 21:5-34.

Harper, D.E. 1970. "Ecological studies of selected level bottom macroinvertebrates off Galveston, Texas," Ph.D. Diss., Texas A&M Univ.

Heck, K.L. 1976. Community structure and the effects of pollution in seagrass meadows and adjacent habitats." *Mar. Biol.* 35:345-357.

Hedgpeth, J.W. 1950. "Notes on the marine invertebrate fauna of salt flat areas in the Aransas National Wildlife Refuge, Texas," *Publ. Inst. Mar. Sci. Texas* 1:103-119.

Hedgpeth, J.W. 1953. "An introduction to zoogeography of the northwestern Gulf of Mexico with reference to the invertebrate fauna," *Publ. Inst. Mar. Sci. Texas* 3:107-224.

Hedgpeth, J.W. 1958. "Estuaries and lagoons. II. Biological aspects," *Geol. Soc. Amer. Mem.* 67; Vol. 1:693-749.

Henry, C.A. 1976. "A study of offshore benthic communities in natural areas and in areas affected by dredging and dredged material disposal." M.S. Thesis, Texas A&M Univ. x + 190 p.

Hildebrand, H.H. 1954. "A study of the fauna of the brown shrimp grounds in the western Gulf of Mexico," *Publ. Inst. Mar. Sci. Texas* 3:225-366.

Hildebrand, H.H. 1955. "A study of the fauna of the pink shrimp grounds in the western Gulf of Mexico," *Publ. Inst. Mar. Sci. Texas* 4:171-232.

Hill, G. 1975. "Animal-sediment relationships." *In* "Environmental assessment of the south Texas outer continental shelf—geologic investigations," U.S.G.S. report to the Bureau of Land Management, Contract No. 08550-MU5-20, p. 133-187.

Hoese, H.D. 1960. "Biotic changes in a bay associated with the end of a drought," *Limnol. Oceanogr.* 5:326-336.

Hoese, H.D., and R.S. Jones. 1963. "Seasonality of larger animals in a Texas turtle grass community," *Publ. Inst. Mar. Sci. Texas* 9:37-47.

Hoese, H.D., B.J. Copeland, et al. 1968. "Fauna of the Aransas Pass Inlet, Texas. 3. Diel and seasonal variations in trawlable organisms of the adjacent area," *Texas J. Sci.* 20:33-60.

Holland, J.S. 1977. "Invertebrate epifauna and macroinfauna." *In* "Environmental studies, South Texas Outer Continental Shelf, Biology and Chemistry," Univ. of Texas final report to the Bureau of Land Management, Contract No. AA550-CT6-17, p. 9-1 to 9-79.

Holland, J.S. 1977. "Invertebrate epifauna and macroinfauna." *In* "Environmental studies, South Texas Outer Continental Shelf, Biology and Chemistry," Univ. of Texas fourth quarterly report for 1976 to the Bureau of Land Management, Contract No. 08550-CT6-17, p. 415-459.

Humm, H.J. 1956. "Sea grasses of the northern Gulf Coast," *Bull. Mar. Sci.* 6:305-308.

Johnson, C.W. 1934. "List of marine mollusca of the Atlantic coast from Labrador to Texas," *Proc. Boston Soc. Nat. Hist.* 40:1-104.

Kalke, R.D. 1972. "Species composition, distribution, and seasonal abundance of macro-zooplankton in intake and discharge areas before and during early operation of the Cedar Bayou generating station," M. Sc. Thesis Texas A&M Univ.

Karlson, R.H. 1978. "Predation and space utilization patterns in a marine epifaunal community." *J. Exp. Mar. Biol. Ecol.* 31:225-239.

Keith, D.E., and N.C. Huling. 1965. "A quantitative study of selected nearshore infauna between Sabine Pass and Bolivar Point, Texas," *Publ. Inst. Mar. Sci. Texas* 10:33-40.

Ladd, H.S. 1951. "Brackish-water and marine assemblages of the Texas coast, with special reference to mollusks," *Publ. Inst. Mar. Sci. Texas* 2:125-163.

Ladd, H.S., J.W. Hedgpeth, and R. Post. 1957. "Environments and facies of existing bays on the central Texas coast," *Geol. Soc. Amer. Mem.* 67, Vol. 2:599-640.

La Fleur, N.C. 1940. "The beach fauna of Grand Isle, La.," *Bios* 11:112-119.

Lebour, M.V. 1922. "The food of plankton organisms," *J. Mar. Biol. Assoc.* U.K. 12:644-677.

Lebour, M.V. 1923. "The food of plankton organisms (Part II)," *J. Mar. Biol. Assoc.* U.K. 13:70-92.

Loesch, H. 1960. "Sporadic mass shoreward migrations of demersal fish and crustaceans in Mobile Bay, Alabama," *Ecology* 41:292-298.

McDougall, K.D. 1943. "Sessile marine invertebrates of Beaufort, N.C.," *Ecol. Monogr.* 13:321-374.

McNulty, J.K. 1961. "Ecological effects of sewage pollution in Biscayne Bay, Florida: sediments and the distribution of benthic and fouling micro-organisms," *Bull. Mar. Sci.* 11:394-447.

Moore, D.R. 1963. "Distribution of the sea grass, *Thalassia,* in the United States," *Bull. Mar. Sci.* 13:329-342.

Nowlin, W.D., and H.J. McClellan. 1967. "A characterization of the Gulf of Mexico waters in winter." *J. Mar. Res.* 25:29-59.

Odum, H.T. 1963. "Productivity measurements in Texas turtle grass and the effects of dredging an intracoastal channel," *Publ. Inst. Mar. Sci. Texas* 9:48-58.

O'Gower, A.K., and J.W. Wacasey. 1967. "Animal communities associated with *Thalassia, Diplanthera,* and sand beds in Biscayne Bay. I. Analysis of communities in relation to water movements." *Bull. Mar. Sci.* 17:175-210.

Oppenheimer, C.H. 1963. "Effects of Hurricane Carla on the ecology of Redfish Bay, Texas," *Bull. Mar. Sci.* 13:59-72.

Osman, R.W. 1977. "The establishment and development of a marine epifaunal community." *Ecol. Monogr.* 47:37-63.

Parker, R.H. 1955. "Changes in the invertebrate fauna, apparently attributable to salinity changes, in the bays of central Texas," *J. Paleont.* 29:193-211.

Parker, R.H. 1959. "Macro-invertebrate assemblages of central Texas coastal bays and Laguna Madre," *Bull. Amer. Assoc. Petrol. Geol.* 43:2100-2166.

Parker, R.H., and J.R. Curray. 1956. "Fauna and bathymetry of banks on the continental shelf, Gulf of Mexico." *Bull. Amer. Assoc. Petrol. Geol.* 40:2428-2439.

Parmer, D.L. 1970. "Some mechanisms of organism limitations in the Inland Houston Ship Channel," M. Sc. Thesis. Texas A&M Univ.

Parmer, D.L., S.H. Hopkins, and R.W. Hann, Jr. 1971. "Biological studies of the Houston Ship Channel," Texas A&M Univ., Estuarine Systems Projects, Tech. Rept. No. 20.

Parr, A.E. 1939. "Quantitative observations on the pelagic Sargassum vegetation of the western North Atlantic," *Bull. Bing. Oceanogr. Coll.* 6:1-94.

Pearse, A.S. 1936. "Estuarine animals at Beaufort, North Carolina," *J. Elisha Mitchell Sci. Soc.* 52:174-222.

Perry, L.M., and J.S. Schwengel. 1955. "Marine shells of the western coast of Florida," *Paleont. Res. Inst.,* Ithaca, N.Y.

Puffer, E.L., and W.K. Emerson. 1953. "The molluscan community of the oyster-reef biotope on the central Texas coast," *J. Paleont.* 27:537-544.

Reid, G.K., Jr. 1955. "A summer study of the biology and ecology of East Bay, Texas. Part I. Introduction, description of the area, methods, some aspects of the fish community, the invertebrate fauna," *Texas J. Sci.* 7:316-343.

Reid, G.K., Jr. 1956. "Ecological investigations in a disturbed Texas coastal estuary," *Texas J. Sci.* 8:296-327.

Richmond, E.A. 1962. "The fauna and flora of Horn Island, Mississippi." *Gulf Res. Repts.* 1:59-106.

Saloman, C.H. 1975. "A selected bibliography of the nearshore environment: Florida West Coast." Misc. Paper No. 5-75, U.S. Army Corps of Engineers.

Sievers, A.M. 1969. "Comparative toxicity of *Gonyaulax monilata* and *Gymnodinium breve* to annelids, crustaceans, mollusks and a fish," *J. Protozool.* 16:401-404.

Simmons, E.G. 1957. "An ecological survey of the upper Laguna Madre of Texas," *Publ. Inst. Mar. Sci. Texas* 4:156-200.

Tabb, D.C., and R.B. Manning. 1961. "A checklist of the flora and fauna of northern Florida Bay and adjacent brackish waters of the Florida mainland collected during the period July, 1957-September, 1960," *Bull. Mar. Sci.* 11:553-648.

Tabb, D.C., and A.C. Jones 1962. "Effect of Hurricane Donna on the aquatic fauna of north Florida Bay," *Trans. Amer. Fish. Soc.* 91:375-378.

Teal, J.M. 1962. "Energy flow in the salt marsh ecosystem of Georgia, *Ecology* 43:614-624.

Thomas, L.P., D.R. Moore, and R.C. Work. 1961. "Effects of Hurricane Donna on the turtle grass beds of Biscayne Bay, Florida," *Bull. Mar. Sci.* 11:191-197.

Torres, J.J., and C.P. Mangum. 1974. "Effects of hyperoxia on survival of benthic marine invertebrates." *Comp. Biochem. Physiol.* (A). 47:17-22.

Weiss, C.M. 1947. "The comparative tolerances of some fouling organisms to copper and mercury," *Biol. Bull.* 93:56-63.

Weiss, J.S. 1968. "Fauna associated with pelagic *Sargassum* in the Gulf Stream," *Amer. Midl. Nat.* 80:554-558.

Wells, H.W. 1961. "The fauna of oyster beds with special reference to the salinity factor," *Ecol. Monogr.* 31:239-266.

Whitten, H.L., H.F. Rosene, and J.W. Hedgpeth. 1950. "The invertebrate fauna of Texas coast jetties; a preliminary survey," *Publ. Inst. Mar. Sci. Texas* 1:53-87.

Williams, H.F. 1951. "The Gulf of Mexico adjacent to Texas." *Tex. J. Sci.* 3:237-250.

Wurtz, C.B., and S.S. Roback. 1955. "The invertebrate fauna of some Gulf Coast rivers," *Proc. Acad. Nat. Sci. Phila.* 107:167-206.

Index

Bold face page numbers indicate illustrations.

Sea whip, 25, **26**
Sergestid shrimp, **48,** 95, **96,** 97
Serpulid worm, 3, 85, **86,** 87, **88,** 91, **93**
Sesarma, **57,** 101, 106
Sessile, 11, 110
Seta, 20, 21, 27, 32, 43, 44, 47, 65, 110
Sharp-knobbed nassa, 40, **41**
Shoal grass, 11, **67**
Shore crab, **81**
Shovelnose lobster, 50, **51**
Shrimp, 5, 37, 39, 40, 73
  arrow, **68**
  brokenback, 59, **68**
  brown, **46**
  caridean, **48**
  cleaning, 13
  grass, 58, **59,** 63
  mantis, 4, **47,** 48
  mud, 62, **63**
  penaeid, **46,** 59, 68
  peppermint, **13**
  pink, **46**
  rock, **47,** 92
  sargassum, **68**
  sergestid, **48,** 95, **96,** 97
  skeleton, **15,** 81
  snapping, 63, **68,** 83, **84**
  sugar, **47**
  white, **46,** 101
Sicyonia, **47,** 92, 106
Simnialena, 16, **26,** 104
Sinum, **64,** 72, 104
Siphon, 21, 29, 30, 52, 54, 60, 100, 111
Siphonaria, 7, **8,** 104
Skeleton shrimp, **15,** 81
Slipper shell (*See also* Atlantic slipper
    shell), **22,** 91, **92**
Snapping shrimp, 63, **68,** 83, **84**
Spadefish, 79, 97
Spanish lobster, 50, **51**
Spartina, **53,** 54, 57, 58
Spat, 9, 13, 87, 89, 91, 111
Speckled crab, **32**
Speckled trout, 59
Spermatophore, 46, 52, 100, 111
Sphaeroma, **9,** 81, 105
Spicule, 17, 75, 111
Spider crab, **33,** 69, 96, 97
Spiochaetopterus, **44,** 103
Spiophanes, 42, **44,** 103
Spirobranchus, 85, **86,** 103
Sponge, 3, 4, 68, 74, 76, 81-84
  boring, 4, 75, 87, 88, 91, **93**
  calcareous, 75
  sulfur, 88, 93

"Sponge" crab, 31
Square-backed crab, 101
Squat isopod, **81**
Squid (*See also* Octopus and Cephalopod),
    39, 99, **100**
Squilla, 5, **47,** 48, 105
Stalked barnacle, (*See also* Gooseneck
    barnacle), **34**
Starfish, 24, **25,** 91
Statocyst, 99, 111
Stenocianops, 94
Stenorynchus, 82, **83,** 106
Stenohaline, 111
Stenolais, 42, **43**
Stomolophus, 33, **96,** 97, 102
Stone crab, 7, **12,** 53, 62, 81, **82, 88,** 89,
    96
Stony coral, 3, 4, **17**
Stout razor, **60**
Striped barnacle, 7
Striped hermit crab, **10,** 69
Strobilization, 96, 111
Stylochus, **89, 94,** 101, 103
Subchelate, 80, 111
Sugar shrimp, **47**
Sulfur sponge, (*See also* Boring sponge),
    88, 93
Surf clam, 40, 44, **61**
Synalpheus, 83, **84,** 106
Synchelium, 50, **105**
Syncoryne, **79,** 102

T

Tagelus, **60,** 105
Tanaid, 91, 92
Tanystylum, **81,** 105
Tarpon, 30
Tectonatica, 104
Tellina, **30,** 44, 104
Telson, 21, 47, 49, 111
Terebra, **44, 64,** 104
Teredo, 34, 105
Texas tusk shell, 72
Thais, 7, 8, 9, **10,** 11, 60, 64, 89, 91, 104
Thalassema, **45,** 46, 107
Thalassia, 2, 11, **67**
Thixotropy, 18, 111
Thyone, **70,** 107
Tiger beetle, **20**
Tollin's wentletrap, **28**
Tonguefish, 39
Tozeuma, **68,** 106
Trachypenaeus, **47,** 106

Trematode, 31, 54, 111
Trochophore, 33, 111
Trypanosyllis, **76,** 103
Tube foot, (*See also* Podium), 14, 25, 85,
    111
Tubularia, **76,** 77, 78, 102
Tulip shell, (*See also* Banded tulip), 26, **28**
Turtle grass, 11, **67**
Two-toned tree oyster, **85**

U & V

Uca, **55, 56,** 57, 106, 107
Umbilicus, 45, 93, 111
Varis, 28, 54, 111
Velella, 34, **35,** 36, 37, 92, 102
Veliger, 22, 57
Venus, cross-barred, **70**
Virgin nerite, 70, **71**

W

Whale, 5
Whelk, 10, 60, 62, 70, **71,** 111
White shrimp, **46,** 101
Widgeon grass, **67**
Willit, 42
Wood crab, 57
Worm, 4, 5, 23, 39, 44, 50, 63, 69, 73, 90
  arrow, 6, 95, **96**
  bamboo, **40**
  blister, 40, 87
  feather duster, 85, **86**
  paddle, **43**
  parchment, **44,** 65, **66**
  peanut, **41**
  proboscis, 5, 63
  ribbon, 62, **63**
  roofing, **42**
  serpulid, 3, 85, **86,** 87, **88,** 91, **93**

XYZ

Xiphopeneus, **47,** 106
Yucatan, 3
Zebra periwinkle (*See also* Littorine and
    Periwinkle), 7, **8**
Zoea, **31,** 55, 11
Zoogeography, 3
Zooid (*See also* Gastrozooid and
    Gonozooid), 15, **16,** 25, 35, 65, 76,
    77, 78, 92, 111
Zooplankton (*See also* Plankter and
    Plankton), 99, 111